ACTIVATED

Iglesia DeJesus

TABLE OF CONTENTS

INSTRUCTIONS

Follow the instructions as outlined because you will quickly repeat this with others who join you in your pursuit of Jesus Christ!

Activated sessions will take place every day for 12 consecutive days, which means one lesson per day. The schedule allows consistency in building up knowledge, revelation, and integrity while laying a sure foundation in the faith.

Start every meeting with prayer. Complete each lesson by reading through the questions and scriptures. New disciples will read the scripture, answer the question, and then write the correct answer in the space provided. You will find the correct answers at the end of each lesson.

At the start of the next session, new disciples will read aloud the questions and answers to their partnering disciple from the prior session. Once complete, move on to the next lesson.

Daily Homework:

New disciples should complete daily homework using the pages provided in the back of the Activated book. As you read through the lesson and scriptures again:

1) On the following line, rewrite the answer.

Example:

19. Why must a person come to Jesus?

A person must come to Jesus so they may have everlasting life. John 3:16-17

The Atonement:
God's Provision for Man's Sin

SESSION

1.

100% of me belongs to Jesus, and He loves me. Song of Songs 7:10

THE ATONEMENT:
God's Provision for Man's Sin

When God created man, he desired to have a family. God spent the first five days of creation preparing a home for His family. In the heavens, the Lord God created the stars, sun, and moon to light the earth. All the beautiful flowers, trees, mountains, rivers, and brilliant colors of the world were prepared and given for the enjoyment and pleasure of the humans He created to be His own. God saw everything He had made and acknowledged that it was good.

Then God placed Adam and Eve in a beautiful garden that the Lord planted. God permitted them to eat from any tree in the garden, including the tree of life. However, one tree God commanded them not to eat: the tree of the knowledge of good and evil. If they ate from it, they would die. God set a choice before His beloved. Adam and Eve could choose to obey God, love Him, and live or disobey God, not love Him, and die.

1) What did Adam and Eve choose to do? *(Genesis 3:3-6)*

_____

_____

_____

2) What was the temptation that drew them into sin? *(Genesis 3:5)*

_____

_____

_____

3) Adam and Eve's sin was based on what three things? *(Genesis 3:6, 1 John 2:16)*

_____

_____

_____

4) What was God doing in the garden, and what was the desire of His heart? *(Genesis 3:8-9)*

_____

_____

_____

The Lord came to the garden to fellowship with them. However, He found that they had disobeyed Him and gone their own way. By turning away from God in disobedience, man lost the blessing and protection of God. Instead, they came under a curse and the power of the devil. They were cast out of the garden and lost fellowship with the Father. Because of Adam and Eve's transgression, the knowledge of good and evil has come to all men, and every unregenerate man has desires bent toward the passing pleasures of sin.

5) What does the scripture teach about the spiritual condition of a man who willfully sins against God? *(Romans 3:10-19, 23)*

a) _____

b) _____

SESSION 1

100% of me belongs to Jesus, and He loves me. Song of Songs 7:10

c) _____

d) _____

e) _____

f) _____

g) _____

h) _____

i) _____

j) _____

k) _____

l) _____

6) If all have sinned willfully and are *not* seeking God, then how can men come to God? *(Isaiah 19:20, John 6:44)*

_____

_____

_____

> Just like in the Garden of Eden when God sought Adam, it is the love and kindness of God that goes out and calls rebellious men to repentance. Read Luke 19:10 and Romans 2:4. God's love strives with the heart of men, convicts them of sin, and draws them to Himself. His love continues to push the stubborn and rebellious man into a corner, pleading with him to surrender his life of sin and death. Yet, God has given man free will, and they can respond how they please--whether life or death.

- **We cannot earn salvation by our good works, nor can we be saved by keeping the law. Here are a few scriptures for reference: Ephesians 2:8-9, Titus 3:5, Galatians 3:21, and Romans 3:20)**

7) Under the old covenant, how was man cleansed from sin and brought into a right relationship with God? *(Leviticus 16:14 - 15; 17:11)*

_____

_____

_____

> From the beginning of time, God instituted the blood sacrifice as atonement for sin. He required the blood of animals because it was pure, innocent, undefiled, and free from a nature bent toward sin. The shedding of this blood brought a temporary covering and atonement for man's sin.

THE NEW COVENANT

8) What did Jesus come to earth to do? *(Matthew 1:21, I John 3:5)*

_____

_____

_____

9) What did John say when he saw Jesus coming toward him? *(John 1:29)*

_____

_____

_____

- **The blood of Jesus is a better sacrifice than the blood of animals. Read Hebrews 9:13-14.**

> The atonement that Jesus made was more significant than the atonement under the old covenant. The temporary forgiveness of sins was already available through the blood of animals, so Jesus' atonement was more than just an offering for the temporary forgiveness of sins. He offers eternal salvation and forgiveness.
>
> The Bible tells us that the life of the flesh is in the blood. The human bloodline comes from the father. In Jesus, there was no sin because He was not born from

Adam or any natural father. The blood of God ran through Jesus' veins. The shed blood of Jesus is for the sins of the world.

10) What did Jesus do for us on the cross? *(I Peter 2:24, Galatians 3:13, Romans 6:6-7)*

a) _____

b) _____

c) _____

11) What is the new covenant Jesus established and made available through His blood?

a) _____

b) _____

c) _____

d) _____

e) _____

f) _____

g) _____

12) How can we become partakers of this new covenant? *(Acts 3:19, Romans 10:9-10)_*

a) _____

b) _____

c) _____

13) Why else did Jesus come to earth? *(John 3:16-17)*

_____

_____

_____

14) Who is under God's judgment? *(John 3:18)*

_____

_____

_____

- This is the judgment [that is, the cause for indictment, the test by which people are judged, the basis for the sentence]: the Light has come into the world, and people loved the darkness rather than the Light, for their deeds were evil. (John 3:19 AMP)

> Under the New Covenant, if men reject God's provision for them, there is no path to salvation. There is no other atonement apart from the cross of Jesus Christ. Only eternal damnation awaits all unrepentant sinners. (Read: Matthew 25:41, Revelation 12:12-15)

15) What is God's desire toward us? *(2 Peter 3:9)*

_____

_____

_____

PRAYER POINTS

- Father God, thank you for sending your Son, who came to seek and save the lost. Thank you for your love and kindness that drew me unto You.

- Thank you for the atoning blood of Jesus, which has redeemed me and freed me from slavery to sin.

- I praise you because it is Your will that none should perish, but that all should come to repentance!

RENUNCIATIONS

- I renounce disobedience and rebellion

- I renounce self-righteousness

SESSION 1

100% of me belongs to Jesus, and He loves me. Song of Songs 7:10

ANSWER KEY

1. Adam and Eve chose to rebel and disobey God. (Genesis 3:3-6)

2. Adam and Eve were tempted to be like God, knowing good and evil. (Genesis 3:5)

3. Adam and Eve's sin was based on the lust of the flesh, the lust of the eyes, and the pride of life. (Genesis 3:6, I John 2:16)

4. God was walking in the garden, calling for Adam, and desiring to be with him. (Genesis 3:8-9)

5. As it is written (Romans 3:10-19, 23):

    a. (v. 10) There is no one who is righteous.

    b. (v. 11) There is no one who understands.

    c. (v. 11) There is no one who seeks after God.

    d. (v. 12) They have all turned aside.

    e. (v. 12) They have together become unprofitable.

    f. (v. 12) There is no one who does good.

    g. (13-14) With their tongues, they have practiced deceit, and their mouth is full of cursing and bitterness.

    h. (15) Their feet are swift to shed blood.

    i. (16) Destruction and misery are in their ways.

    j. (17) The way of peace they have not known.

    k. (18) There is no fear of God before their eyes.

    l. (23) All have sinned and fall short of the glory of God.

6. God sent Jesus as Savior, and no one can come to Jesus unless the Father who sent Him draws him. (Isaiah 19:20, John 6:44)

7. Under the old covenant, a man was cleansed from sin and brought into right relationship with God through the atoning blood of animals.(Leviticus 16:14 - 15; 17:11)

8. Jesus came to save His people from their sins. (Matthew 1:21, I John 3:5)

9. John said, "Behold! The Lamb of God who takes away the sin of the world!" (John 1:29)

10. The work Jesus did for us on the cross (I Peter 2:24, Galatians 3:13, Romans 6:6-7) :

     a. He bore our sins in His own body

     b. He redeemed us from the curse of the law

     c. He freed our bodies of sin that we should no longer be slaves of sin

11. The new covenant Jesus establish through his blood (Hebrews 8:8-12, Ezekiel 36:26-27):

     a. (v. 10) He puts His laws in their mind and writes them on their hearts.

     b. (v. 10) He will be their God, and they shall be His people.

c.   (v. 11) For all shall know God, from the least of them to the greatest of them.

d.   (v. 12) He will be merciful to their unrighteousness, and their sins and their lawless deeds He will remember no more.

e.   (v. 26) He will give you a new heart and put a new spirit within you.

f.   (v. 26) He will take the heart of stone out of your flesh and give you a heart of flesh.

g.   (v. 27) He will put His Spirit within you and cause you to walk in His statutes, and you will keep His judgments and do them.

12.   We can become a partaker of the new covenant by (Acts 3:19, Romans 10:9-10):

a.   We must repent and be converted.

b.   We must confess with our mouth that Jesus is Lord.

c.   We must believe in our heart God has raised Jesus from the dead.

13.   Jesus came so the world might be saved and have eternal life through Him. (John 3:16-17)

14.   Those who do not believe in the name of the Son of God are under God's judgment and are already condemned. (John 3:18)

15.   God desires that none should perish but that all should come to repentance. (II Peter 3:9)

Who is Jesus?

2.

WHO IS JESUS?

People study the scriptures because they believe it will give them eternal life; however, the scriptures testify to us about Jesus, the person. We must seek the One who the scripture declares, for He is the One who has the eternal life we desire. In reading the scriptures, we come face to face with Jesus Christ and are invited to build a personal relationship with Him.

The scriptures are the perfect and holy words of God, which every believer must endeavor to know. The scriptures point to Jesus, and we pursue Him through obedience, prayer, worship, communion, and fasting. Our pursuit of Jesus will lead us back to the scriptures, which will lead us back to Him.

JESUS THE PERSON

To be transformed, we must contend for the invisible image of Jesus Christ. It is essential to believe in Jesus for who He truly is and not what we presuppose about Him. As disciples, we must fight for the true essence of who He is to be established in our hearts, not the false imagery the world gives.

1) What was in the beginning, and who was it? *(John 1:1)*

_____

_____

_____

2) Who became flesh and dwelt among us? *(John 1:14)*

_____

_____

_____

3) Who was manifested in the flesh? *(1 Timothy 3:16)*

_____

_____

_____

4) What were some of the things that people said about Jesus? *(John 7:40-41)*

_____

_____

_____

5) What did Jesus say people search for in the scriptures? *(John 5:39)*

_____

_____

_____

6) Jesus said the scriptures testify of whom? *(John 5:39)*

_____

_____

_____

7) Why must a person come to Jesus? *(John 5:40)*

_____

_____

_____

SESSION 2

100% of me belongs to Jesus, and He loves me. Song of Songs 7:10

Note: The world system views religion as a set of principles that people use to forge wonderful and meaningful lives. Amazingly enough, that life will dry up if the individual does not develop a personal relationship with Jesus. Those seeking to follow Jesus must guard against the peril of being drawn away after mere ideas or philosophies. Therefore, we rely on scripture which has established that Jesus is not a book, religion, or a set of beliefs.

THE WAY OF THE CROSS

Jesus has clear intentions in the lives of those who love and follow Him. He demands absolute obedience, devotion, and sacrifice. His demands can be challenging for us because we have our desires, strongholds in thought, and past experiences. Nevertheless, the born-again believer has everything needed to confront these challenges, deny themself, and follow Jesus on the way of the Cross.

8) What problem did Peter have? *(Matthew 16:23)*

_____

_____

_____

9) What did Jesus say had to be done before taking up your cross? *(Matthew 16:24)*

_____

_____

_____

10) What does a person become after they sincerely deny themselves and take up their cross? *(Mark 8:34)*

_____

_____

_____

11) What must you do if you want to save your life? *(Mark 8:35)*

_____

_____

_____

12) How often should a person take up his cross? *(Luke 9:23)*

_____

_____

_____

13) How often will you have to deny yourself if you are going to take up your cross daily? *(Luke 9:23)*

_____

_____

_____

> Though the act of "denying yourself" can appear in many forms, it always fits the description of self-denial. Jesus' encounter with the rich young ruler illustrates this. Read Mark 10:17-23.

14) What did the rich young ruler think about Jesus? *(Mark 10:17)*

_____

_____

_____

15) Did the rich young ruler live a good, moral life? How did Jesus feel about him *(Mark 10:19-21)*?

_____

_____

_____

16) What did Jesus require of this young man in terms of self-denial before him taking up his cross and following Jesus? *(Mark 10:21)*

_____

_____

_____

SESSION 2

100% of me belongs to Jesus, and He loves me. Song of Songs 7:10

17) How did the rich young ruler respond? *(Mark 10:22)*

_____

_____

_____

18) How did Jesus respond? *(Mark 10:23)}*

_____

_____

_____

> The rich young ruler lived an exceptionally moral life and even sought out Jesus. Nevertheless, he did not see the benefit of forgiveness and following Jesus as something worthy of self-denial.
>
> Perhaps you have done this on some level, but one thing is sure--anyone who has dismissed the heart of God must repent immediately and continue their walk in the way of the cross.
>
> Jesus is worth everything! Occasionally, He may call us to show that we believe He is worth everything in a big way like the rich young ruler, but we prove He is worthy daily by denying ourselves, taking up our cross, and following Him.

- **For the rest of your life, God is going to use you to share your testimony and the Gospel of Jesus Christ with the people you love. These questions will help you to record your testimony, the most meaningful event in your life. They will equip you to better understand and share effectively. Answer them thoughtfully and thoroughly in your notebook tonight!**

MY LIFE BEFORE CHRIST

1) What about my life before Christ will relate most to the non-Christians with whom I am sharing?

a) What sorts of sins did I struggle with?

_____

_____

_____

b) What did I think of Christianity?

_____

_____

_____

c) Was I raised in church?

_____

_____

_____

d) What life path was I on? Was it triumphant or tragic?

_____

_____

_____

e) What other appropriate information can I share that will accurately depict what my life was life before Christ?

_____

_____

_____

2) What did my life revolve around, and name three things that were most important to me?

_____

_____

_____

3) Where did I get my security, identity, or happiness?

_____

_____

_____

SESSION 2

100% of me belongs to Jesus, and He loves me. Song of Songs 7:10

4) In what ways do I see those things differently? How were they going to let me down?

_____

_____

_____

PRAYER POINTS

- Lord, I thank you that eternal life is knowing the One true God, Jesus Christ, the One you sent. Help me to believe Jesus as the scriptures have revealed Him to be.

- Father, let me see You as You are so I can be transformed into the true image of the Son.

- I declare I will deny myself, take up my cross, and follow Jesus.

RENUNCIATIONS

- I renounce every false image that does not testify of Jesus.

- I renounce the way that seems right, but the end is destruction and not life.

ANSWER KEY

1. In the beginning was the Word, and the Word was God. (John 1:1)

2. The Word became flesh and dwelt among us. (John 1:14)

3. God was manifested in the flesh. (1 Timothy 3:16)

4. Many people said of Jesus, "Truly this is the Prophet," and others said, "This is the Christ." (John 7:40-41)

5. Jesus said people search the scriptures for eternal life. (John 5:39)

6. Jesus said the scriptures testify of Him. (John 5:39)

7. A person must come to Jesus that they may have life. (John 5:40)

8. Peter was not mindful of the things of God but the things of men. (Matthew 16:23)

9. Jesus said you must deny yourself before taking up your cross. (Matthew 16:24)

10. After a person sincerely denies themself and takes up their cross, they become a follower of Jesus. (Mark 8:34)

11. You must lose your life for Jesus' sake and the gospel's to save your life. (Mark 8:35)

12. A person must take up their cross daily. (Luke 9:23)

13. If I am going to take up my cross daily, I will have to deny myself daily. (Luke 9:23)

14. The rich young ruler thought Jesus was a good teacher. (Mark 10:17)

15. The rich young ruler lived a good and moral life, and Jesus loved him. (Mark 10:19-21)

16. Before picking up his cross and following Him, Jesus required the young man to sell whatever he had and give to the poor. (Mark 10:21)

17. The rich young ruler was sad, and he went away sorrowful. (Mark 10:22)

18. Jesus said to His disciples that it is hard for those who have riches to enter the Kingdom of God. (Mark 10:23)

The Lordship
of Jesus.

3.

THE LORDSHIP OF JESUS

The Lordship of Jesus Christ denotes He is the sovereign ruler and authority over everything, including His followers' lives.

Read Philippians 2:9-11, 2 Corinthians 4:5, and Acts 2:36.

FEAR OF THE LORD

The Lordship of Jesus and the fear of the Lord go together. It means to be in awe of Him, give Him the highest reverence, and honor Him. Psalms 9:10 says: "The fear of the LORD is the beginning of wisdom: and the knowledge of the holy is understanding." We must fear the One with all power.

1) According to Jesus, who are we to fear and why? *(Luke 12:5, Matthew 10:28)*

_____

_____

_____

2) What judgment seat must we all appear before? *(2 Corinthians 5:10)*

_____

_____

_____

3) What explanation does the scripture provide for persuading others to serve Jesus.
   (2 Corinthians 5:11)

_____

_____

_____

4) In preaching the Gospel, what did Peter say about Jesus? *(Acts 2:36)*

_____

_____

_____

5) When they heard this preaching, what happened and what was their response?
   (Acts 2:37)

_____

_____

_____

6) What was Peter's response to the question asked? *(Acts 2:38)*

_____

_____

_____

LORDSHIP

When a person becomes a believer, they confess the Lordship of Jesus and acknowledge He has complete control of their lives. They commit to laying down

SESSION 3

100% of me belongs to Jesus, and He loves me. Song of Songs 7:10

their will and desires to live with Him as their Lord and Master. A committed disciple is devoted to doing His bidding, not their own.

7) What are the rewards promised to those who have forsaken all to follow Christ? *(Matthew 19:27-29, Mark 10:28-30)*

a) _____

b) _____

c) _____

8) Jesus gave the right to become _____ to those who _____ *(John 1:12)*

9) If we open our hearts to receive Jesus, what promise has He given us? *(Revelation 3:20)*

_____

_____

_____

10) Unless one is born of _____ and the _____, he cannot enter the Kingdom of God. *(John 3:3-7)*

11) When we receive Jesus, what gift does God give? *(1 John 5:11; Romans 6:23)*

_____

_____

_____

REPENTANCE

The act of repentance is to turn from sin. It is more than a feeling of sorrow and regret. True repentance involves a complete change of direction.

12) How does the Word of God define repentance (*Psalm 32:5; Proverbs. 28:13, Ezekiel 18:21-23,27-28)*?

_____

_____

_____

13) If we confess our sins, what will God do? *(I John 1:9)*

_____

_____

_____

14) If we are willing and obedient, what else will the Lord do? *(Isaiah 1:18-19)*

_____

_____

_____

15) To live, what must the wicked man do? *(Ezekiel 33:15)*

_____

_____

_____

16) What are the conditions set so God can dwell in us and walk among us? *(2 Corinthians 6:14-18)*

_____

_____

_____

> We see that God and His conditions are unchanging. This exact requirement was made of the Israelites when they were going to possess the land God had given them.

17) What did God require of the Israelites when they entered a land to possess it? *(Deuteronomy 7:1-3)*

_____

_____

_____

SESSION 3

100% of me belongs to Jesus, and He loves me. Song of Songs 7:10

18) Why did God require this? *(Deuteronomy 7:4,6; Deuteronomy 8:1)*

_____

_____

_____

> The conditions for repentance are demonstrated clearly in the parable about the lost son.

19) What happened to the son's life after he received his inheritance and left his father's house? *(Luke 15:11-16)*

_____

_____

_____

20) What did the lost son decide to do when he realized his condition? *(Luke 15:17-19)*

_____

_____

_____

21) When the son returned home, what did his father do? *(Luke 15:20)*

_____

_____

_____

22) What happened after the son confessed his sin? *(Luke 15:22-24)*

_____

_____

_____

RESTITUTION

> Restitution is made as God instructs and leads. Zaccheus was familiar with the prophet Ezekiel's teaching of repentance and restitution. Zaccheus was a wicked man, a tax collector, and had a reputation for treating people unjustly.

23) When Jesus told Zacchaeus He would stay at his house, what was Zaccheus' response that showed his repentant heart? *(Luke 19: 1-8)*

_____

_____

_____

24) What did Jesus say to Zaccheus? *(Luke 19:9-10)*

_____

_____

_____

PERSONAL EXPERIENCE – HOW I CAME TO CHRIST

Question/Answer

1. When was the first time I heard the Gospel, and what was my initial reaction?

_____

_____

_____

2. What did I realize when I heard it?

_____

_____

_____

3. Why did I decide to give myself to Christ and give Him complete control of my life?

_____

_____

_____

PRAYER POINTS

- **Lord, You are sovereign and worthy of all glory, power, and honor! Help me to fear You and walk softly before You.**

- I declare that You are my master (boss), and I will lay down my will and desires for Your will and desires.

- Father, let humility and true repentance be an active part of my walk with You. When faced with the need to change, let godly sorrow lead me to change.

- I declare I will bear fruits worthy of repentance.

ANSWER KEY

1. Jesus said, "Fear Him who, after He has killed, has power to cast into hell" and destroy both soul and body in hell. (Luke 12:5, Matthew 10:28)

2. We must all appear before the judgment seat of Christ. (2 Corinthians 5:10)

3. Knowing the terror of the Lord, we persuade others. (2 Corinthians 5:11)

4. God has made this Jesus both Lord and Christ. (Acts 2:36)

5. They were cut to the heart and asked, "What must we do?" (Acts 2:37)

6. Peter said, "Repent, and let every one of you be baptized in the name of Jesus Christ for the remission of sins, and you shall receive the gift of the Holy Spirit." (Acts 2:38)

7. The rewards promised to those who have forsaken all to follow Christ (Matthew 19:27-29, Mark 10:28-30):

   a. They shall rule and reign with Him.

   b. They shall receive 100 times as much in this present age as they have given up.

   c. They shall receive eternal life.

8. Jesus gave the right to become children of God to those who believe in His name. (John 1:12)

9. He has promised to come in and dine (or have fellowship) with us. (Revelation 3:20)

10. Unless one is born of water and the Spirit, he cannot enter the Kingdom of God. (John 3:3-7)

11. He gives eternal life in Christ Jesus, our Lord. (1 John 5:11; Romans 6:23)

12. Repentance means acknowledging, confessing, and forsaking our sin by turning away from all transgressions. (Psalm 32:5; Proverbs. 28:13)

13. If we confess our sins, He will forgive us of our sins and cleanse us from all unrighteousness. (1 John 1:9)

14. He will make our sins white as snow, and we will eat the good of the land. (Isaiah 1:18-19)

15. He must restore the pledge, give back what he has stolen, and walk in the statutes of life without committing iniquity. (Ezekiel 33:15)

16. We are commanded not to be unequally yoked together with unbelievers, come out from among them, be separate, and not touch what is unclean. (2 Corinthians 6:14-18)

17. He required that they make no covenant, show no mercy, and not allow intermarrying to take place. (Deuteronomy 7:1-3)

18. God required this because the heathen nations would turn their sons away from following Him to serve other gods. God's people were to be holy, set aside for the Lord alone so that they would live, multiply, and possess the land God had for them. (Deut 7:4,6; Deut 8:1)

19. The son wasted all of his possessions with prodigal living. He was sent into the fields to feed the swine, and he longed to eat what they ate, but no one gave him anything. (Luke 15:11-16)

20. When he finally came to his senses, he decided to leave his sinful ways, go to his father, and confess his sin. (Luke 15:17-19)

21. When he was still a great way off, his father saw him and had compassion, and ran and fell on his neck and kissed him. (Luke 15:20)

22. His father restored him, made him a son, and the household celebrated. (Luke 15:22-24)

23. He received Jesus gladly, saying that he would give half his possessions to the poor, and if he had defrauded anyone, he would give back four times as much. (Luke 19: 1-8)

24. Jesus said salvation has come to his house and the Son of Man has come to seek and to save the lost. (Luke 19:9-10)

Becoming a Disciple.

SESSION

100% of me belongs to Jesus, and He loves me. Song of Songs 7:10

4.

BECOMING A DISCIPLE

First and foremost, discipleship is a call to follow Jesus. One must endeavor to be obedient to His written word and the Holy Spirit. In our obedience, we have relationships with people who help in our pursuit of Christ. For them to be effective, the Lord permits them to have authority and influence in our lives to bring instruction, correction, and improvement so we may flourish in following Christ. This describes a disciple-teacher relationship.

DEFINING A DISCIPLE

Additionally, a disciple is also the follower of a teacher, a disciplined one. Merely following a teaching does not define a disciple because that would eliminate the need for relationships.

1) What two things did Jesus say His disciples would do? *(John 14:12)*

_____

_____

_____

2) What is one of the ways disciples glorify the Father? *(John 15:8)*

_____

_____

_____

3) As a disciple matures, who does he become more like? *(Luke 6:40)*

_____

_____

_____

WHAT IS DISCIPLESHIP?

Discipleship describes the teaching and learning process by which a believer becomes more like Christ in every area of their life.

4) Who is the head of the church? *(Colossians 1:18, Ephesians 1:22)*

_____

_____

_____

5) When a person becomes a disciple, who do they follow? *(1 Thessalonians 1:6)*

_____

_____

_____

6) As followers of Christ, are you able to influence those who believe? *(1 Thessalonians 1:7)*

_____

_____

_____

7) Who did Paul tell the disciples to follow, and under what conditions were they to do it? *(1 Corinthians 11:1)*

_____

_____

_____

8) What was Paul's expectation of the disciples in Corinth? *(2 Corinthians 2:9)*

_____

_____

_____

OBEDIENCE AND SUBMISSION

To flourish in any tribe, family, church community, team, or business, a person must know how and where they fit in. Many failures in a Christian's life are rooted in a lack of love and not being submitted to authority. When we fail to recognize authority, we set ourselves up to fall short continuously. Immaturity and carnality cause us to only respond to worldly authority; someone must control us before submitting to them. However, it is different with a spiritually mature Christian.

9) If someone loves Jesus, will they keep His commands and words? *(John 14:21, 23)*

_____

_____

10) How do you know if someone does not love Jesus? *(John 14:24)*

_____

_____

11) What requirement does Jesus make of friends? *(John 15:14)*

_____

_____

_____

12) How is kingdom authority established? *(Luke 22:26-27, Matthew 20:26)*

_____

_____

_____

13) Who is worthy of double honor? *(1 Timothy 5:17)*

_____

_____

_____

> God's throne is established on His authority, and His authority represents God Himself. God does things decently and in order. He expects His disciples to do the same. We have leaders to imitate and are commanded to obey them as they follow Christ.

14) What did the scribes say about Jesus, and what was His response? *(Mark 3:22, 28-30)*

_____

_____

_____

- **What is blasphemy of the Holy Spirit? Knowingly, not mistakenly, attributing the work of the Holy Spirit to Satan.**

15) What are believers instructed to do in this passage, and why? *(Hebrews 13:7, 17)*

_____

_____

_____

> As Christians, we do not violate God's authority or come into agreement with Satan's ways. Far too often, highly deceived people claim to stand with Christ in doctrine and confession while standing with Satan in principle and practice. Some people know the Bible but refuse submission to Jesus or anyone who represents Him. The greatest of God's demands on humanity is not that he makes offerings and sacrifices but something better.

SESSION 4

100% of me belongs to Jesus, and He loves me. Song of Songs 7:10

16) What is better than sacrifice? *(1 Samuel 15:22)*

_____

_____

_____

> As God's children and servants, the first thing we meet is His authority. When we become acquainted with authority, we will recognize it everywhere and submit to it.

17) Whose authority did Jesus honor by answering the High Priest? *(Matthew 26:62-63)*

_____

_____

_____

LESSONS TO LEARN CONCERNING AUTHORITY

> Whenever believers gather, spiritual order immediately falls into place. As Christians, we know who is in authority and under our authority. Once we learn submission to authority, we naturally find our place in the body.

- **Authority in the Kingdom is established by the submission of a disciple, not the strength or giftedness of a teacher.**

> Christians practice obedience while others are like savages who cannot obey. They are carnal and at enmity against the laws of God. Disciples do not feel bound regardless of where they are placed in light of godly authority. The obedience of their heart helps them understand they are being led and cared for, not controlled.

MEASURING OUR OBEDIENCE

> We must know our leaders. Knowing them allows us to be aware if they have betrayed God and are attempting to lead us astray with them. With the reality of rebellion, worldliness, and apostasy, leaders must be right with God. When leaders are right with God, it makes obedience a lot easier. There is no example in scripture

that states or implies a leader was right with God yet their godly authority had to be dishonored by those in their care.

18) If a man wants you to do something contrary to God and His word, what should you do? *(Acts 5:29)*

_____

_____

_____

SUBMISSION IS AN ABSOLUTE ATTITUDE OF THE HEART

Only God receives absolute obedience. Everyone else receives qualified obedience in relation to where they are concerning God. This is not a comparison of our feelings about their instructions but their standing in relation to God and His Word.

We submit to those in authority, and we must never do things that offend God.

Personal Reflection: Would I like to lead someone like myself?

PRAYER POINTS

- Lord, I thank You for the body of Christ that helps me flourish as I follow You. I thank You that You discipline those You love, and I want to be loved by You in every way.

- Father, let me have a spirit of obedience that delights You.

- I declare that I will be a submissive and obedient disciple of Jesus Christ.

- I declare I will bear fruit and glorify my Father in heaven.

RENUNCIATIONS

- I renounce lawlessness and dishonor.

- I renounce stubbornness and idolatry.

SESSION 4

100% of me belongs to Jesus, and He loves me. Song of Songs 7:10

ANSWER KEY

1. Jesus said His disciples would do the works that He did and greater works. (John 14:12)

2. Disciples glorify the Father when they bear much fruit. (John 15:8)

3. A disciple will be like their teacher as they mature. (Luke 6:40)

4. Jesus Christ is the head of the church. (Colossians 1:18, Ephesians 1:22)

5. Disciples follow the Lord and their teacher. 1(Thessalonians 1:6)

6. Yes. As followers of Christ, we become examples to others. (1 Thessalonians 1:7)

7. Paul said, "Imitate me, just as I also imitate Christ." (1 Corinthians 11:1)

8. Paul expected obedience in all things. (2 Corinthians 2:9)

9. Yes. If you love Him, you will keep His commands and words. (John 14:21, 23)

10. If someone does not love Jesus, they will not keep His words. (John 14:24)

11. Jesus said, "You are My friends if you do whatever I command you." (John 15:14)

12. In the Kingdom, authority is established through servanthood. (Luke 22:26-27, Matt 20:26)

13. Elders who rule well will be counted worthy of double honor, especially those who labor in the word and doctrine. (1 Timothy 5:17)

14. The scribes said He has Beelzebub and said He casts out demons by the ruler of demons. Jesus responded and said, "he who blasphemes against the Holy Spirit never has forgiveness, but is subject to eternal condemnation." (Mark 3:22, 28-30)

15. Believers are instructed to remember those who rule over us and have spoken the word of God to us. We should also consider the outcome of their lives and follow their faith. (Hebrews 13:7, 17)

16. Obedience is better than sacrifice. (1 Samuel 15:22)

17. Jesus honored the authority of the living God. (Matthew 26:62-63)

18. You should obey God rather than men. (Acts 5:29)

God's Government:
and Order for the Church

5.

GOD'S GOVERNMENT:
AND ORDER FOR THE CHURCH

Read Ephesians 1:22, 4:15; Colossians 1:18; and Titus 1:5.

The Lord is clear about how His church is to be organized and facilitated. First, Christ is the head of the church and its supreme authority. Second, the local church is autonomous, free from any external authority or control beyond her apostles' and elders' loving influence. Third, the local church is governed by spiritual leadership consisting of two main groups—elders and deacons.

1) What types of officials are set in the body of Christ to watch over and instruct the saints? And what are their responsibilities? *(Ephesians 4:11-12)*

_____

_____

_____

2) How long will the ministry of the elders be in operation in the church? What will happen because of these ministries? *(Ephesians 4:13-15)*

_____

_____

_____

3) What office of oversight has God appointed for the local church *(Acts 14:23)*

_____

_____

_____

4) What are the responsibilities of the Elders? *(Acts 20:28, Hebrews 13:17)*

_____

_____

_____

5) As a watchman of the flock of God, what specifically are the elders to do? *(Ezekiel 33:2-7)*

_____

_____

_____

6) If the watchman fails to warn the people, whose fault is it, and who is held accountable? *(Ezekiel 33:5-7)*

_____

_____

_____

SESSION 5

100% of me belongs to Jesus, and He loves me. Song of Songs 7:10

7) If the people under his oversight refused to take warning from their elders, who is responsible? *(Ezekiel 33:2-4)*

_____

_____

_____

8) What are members of the body urged to do? *(Hebrews 13:17, I Peter 5:5)*

_____

_____

_____

9) What should our attitude be toward those who are teaching us and leading us in the ways of God? *(Hebrews 13:7)*

_____

_____

_____

Note: Jesus preaches that those appointed as leaders in the church must be different from the heathen. Contrast the proper attitude against the wrong attitude. Read Matthew 20:25-28.

EXAMPLES OF BIBLICAL GOVERNING

The priesthood of every believer is a feature of the new covenant. Any attitude that causes Christians to seek spiritual guidance apart from Christ and His government tends to make them solely dependent on men. There is a place in each believer's life for the personal guidance and direction of the Holy Spirit.

The Bible teaches that the things that happen to Israel have been for our example. Their example of governing the people is a good one to follow.

■ **Older women are to counsel younger women in matters concerning their relationships. Likewise, the men are to advise men regarding relationships. Any cases that are too difficult or cannot be settled must be brought before the elders for judgment for further discernment and discretion.**

In *Foxe's Book of Martyrs*, John returned from exile on Patmos, and he went to a specific city. There he committed a young man into the bishop of the church's charge, asking him to take spiritual oversight of the young man. The bishop took him to his home, baptized him, and nourished him. However, after a while, he relaxed his care for the boy. Now having more liberty, the young man fell in with his old friends who were hardened in sin. He began attending their lawless banquets. They rob and steal, and the young man became like an unbroken wild horse without a harness. He left the way of salvation and went with the band of thieves committing murder and other wicked crimes.

When the apostle John returned later, he asked the Bishop to present his charge. The bishop thought he meant some money. John said, "the young man, the soul of our brother I committed to your custody, I do require." When John learned what had happened, he said, "a fine keeper of his brother's soul have I left here!" He then asked for a horse and guards so he could be taken to the highway where the gang of robbers lay watch. John was overtaken by the thieves, dismounted, and said, "take me to your captain." As soon as the young man saw John, he was stricken with shame and began to run. But John, forgetting his age, began to run after him saying, "my son, do not fear, there is still hope for your salvation. I will answer to Christ for you, and if need be, I will die for you as Christ has died for us. Believe me; Christ has sent me." The young man stopped, began to weep bitterly, dropped his weapons, and embraced John crying through repentance. John brought him back to the church, and after praying for him daily with fasting and prayer, he restored him to the church and left him as proof of regeneration.

In the Church, it is not the attitude that all truth must come from leaders. The Holy Spirit is given to each member of the body to lead each member into all truth. In this parable, there was no fear for the 99 who were safely in the fold but great concern for the one that strayed away. Guarding the flock is watching diligently lest any member should stumble in sin.

10) What did the shepherd do when he realized one of his sheep had strayed away? *(Matthew 18:12)*

_____

_____

_____

SESSION 5

100% of me belongs to Jesus, and He loves me. Song of Songs 7:10

CONFRONTING SIN IN THE CHURCH

> God's holiness is the dominant theme in the Bible, and those who belong to the body of Christ live holy lives. 1 Peter 1:15-16 declares, "Be holy for I am holy." As the body of Christ, the church must practice biblical discipline toward professing Christians who are found in persistent sin.

11) With whom are believers not to associate? *(I Corinthians 5:9–11)*

_____

_____

_____

12) What did Paul say would happen if sin and evil behavior remains in the church? *(I Corinthians 5:1–6)*

_____

_____

_____

13) Who are we to judge, and who does God judge? *(I Corinthians 5:12-13)*

_____

_____

_____

14) What should you do if you know a member of the church is caught in unrepentant sin? *(Matthew 18:15 – 17)*

a) _____

b) _____

c) _____

d) _____

15) What are we to do with those "brothers/sisters" who refused to repent of their wickedness? *(I Corinthians 5:13)*

_____

_____

_____

16) If a brother or sister is caught in sin and desires to be restored, how should they be treated? *(Galatians 6:1)*

_____

_____

_____

17) What does Jesus say about removing those who will not repent, even if they are important members of the body? *(Matthew 5:29 – 30)*

_____

_____

_____

18) What are the disciples urged to do? *(I Corinthians 5: 6-8)*

_____

_____

_____

> God had forbidden Israel to take any spoil from the city of Jericho. Yet, some Israelites acted unfaithfully to this command and took some of the things that had been banned. This action (sin in the camp) caused the whole assembly of Israel to be defeated by their enemies. This is the same principle outlined in the New Testament. If sin and rebellion can remain in the church, the whole body is in danger of being infected, and the church will be defeated before its enemies.
>
> Read Joshua 7.

19) What happened to the Israelites who went up against Ai? *(Joshua 7:4-5)*

_____

_____

_____

SESSION 5

100% of me belongs to Jesus, and He loves me. Song of Songs 7:10

20) What reason did God give Joshua for this defeat? *(Joshua 7:11-12)*

_____

_____

_____

21) What condition did God set before Israel for continuing to be with them? *(Joshua 7:12-15)*

_____

_____

_____

GOD'S DISCIPLINE PROVES HIS LOVE

22) Why does God discipline us? *(Hebrews 12:5-10)*

_____

_____

_____

23) What feeling do we have when we are disciplined, and what does discipline yield? *(Hebrews 12:11)*

_____

_____

_____

MY LIFE AFTER COMING TO CHRIST

1. How is my life different now? List specific changes in your character, attitude, and perspective on life.

_____

_____

_____

2. What motivates me now? What do I live for?

_____

_____

_____

3. How does knowing Christ help me deal with challenges?

_____

_____

_____

PRAYER POINTS

• **Father, I thank You for setting spiritual leadership in the church to watch over and instruct me.**

• **I will obey and be submissive to those who watch over my soul.**

• **Lord, I commit to cleaning out any malice and wickedness to preserve the feast of sincerity and truth.**

• **I declare I will endure discipline to bring forth the peaceable fruits of righteousness.**

SESSION 5

100% of me belongs to Jesus, and He loves me. Song of Songs 7:10

ANSWER KEY

1. The Lord has given some to be apostles, prophets, evangelists, pastors, and teachers. They are responsible for equipping the saints for the work of ministry and for edifying the body of Christ. (Ephesians 4:11-12)

2. The ministry of elders will continue until we all come to the unity of the faith and of the knowledge of the Son of God, and because of these ministries, we will no longer be children, tossed to and fro by deceitful men. Instead, we will speak the truth in love and grow up in all things into Him who is the head—Christ. (Ephesians 4:13-15)

3. God has appointed elders for the local church. (Acts 14:23)

4. Elders are responsible as overseers who shepherd the church, watch over the saint's souls, and give an account to God for them. (Acts 20:28, Hebrews 13:17)

5. As a watchman, an elder's responsibility is to see the sword coming and warn the people. (Ezekiel 33:2-7)

6. The watchman will be held accountable if he fails to warn the people. (Ezekiel 33:5-7)

7. Whoever refuses to listen to the watchman is held accountable. (Ezekiel 33:2-4)

8. Members of the body are urged to obey those who watch over their souls and submit to them. (Hebrews 13:17, I Peter 5:5)

9. We should consider the outcome of our leaders' conduct and imitate their faith. (Hebrews 13:7)

10. The shepherd left the 99 and went in search of the one that had gone astray. (Matthew 18:12)

11. Believers are not to associate with any so-called brother or sister who is sexually immoral, covetous, an idolater, reviler, drunkard, or a swindler. (I Corinthians 5:9–11)

12. If sinful behavior is allowed to remain in the church, it will bring forth more evil, and like leaven, it will filter through the whole community. (I Corinthians 5:1–6)

13. Believers judge those within the church, and God will judge those outside the church, the sinners. (I Corinthians 5:12-13)

14. a. If your brother sins against you, go and tell him his fault between you and him alone.

    b. If he refuses to listen, take one or two more with you.

    c. If he refuses to listen to them, tell it to the church.

    d. If he refuses even to hear the church, let him be to you like a heathen and a tax collector. (Matthew 18:15 – 17)

15. If a brother or sister refuses to repent, we remove the wicked person from among ourselves. (I Corinthians 5:13)

16. They should be restored in a spirit of gentleness with humility while considering ourselves lest we also are tempted. (Galatians 6:1)

17. It is better to cut off even the most critical members of the body than cause the whole body to be cast into Hell because of the spreading wickedness. (Matthew 5:29 – 30)

18. Disciples are urged to clean out the old leaven of malice and wickedness and keep the feast of sincerity and truth. (I Corinthians 5: 6-8)

19. The Israelites fled before the men of Ai, and 36 men were killed. (Joshua 7:4-5)

20. God told Joshua that Israel was defeated because they stole the accursed things and deceived others by putting the items among their belongings. (Joshua 7:11-12)

21. God commanded that the accursed things and the people who took them to be destroyed with fire. (Joshua 7:12-15)

22. God disciplines us for our good, and so we may share in His holiness. (Hebrews 12:5-10)

23. At the moment, discipline is not joyful, but it yields the peaceable fruit of righteousness. (Hebrews 12:11)

Baptism
in Water.

6.

BAPTISM IN WATER

When we come to Jesus and repent of our sins, we become what the Bible calls "born again." We have a new birth and receive a new heart. Jesus comes to dwell in our hearts by faith as we become partakers of eternal life. (John 3:3; Ephesians 3:17; Colossians 1:12; 1 John 5:11-13)

As Jesus Christ hung on the cross, He became sin on our behalf (2 Corinthians 5:21). Jesus died to make perfect atonement for man's sinful and lost condition. He was buried in a tomb, and on the third day, He rose from the dead and triumphed over Satan, thereby providing for man's salvation. Because we receive His life when we make Jesus Lord, our relationship with God is made alive.

Circumcision in the natural sense is the cutting away of the unnecessary and unclean part, the foreskin of the man. In the spiritual sense, circumcision is a cutting away of the sin-loving nature. Even more, baptism is a burial and resurrection. Baptism is a total dying of the old self by union with Christ--a real and present rising again by participation in His risen life. As we partake in water baptism, we share Jesus' burial and resurrection. Sin no longer has dominion over us because we now share the resurrection life of Jesus.

The baptisms throughout the New Testament were all done by immersion of the entire body beneath the water. The water represents the grave where the burial takes place. We experience a burial of our old nature and a rising to walk with Christ in the newness of life. Water baptism does not grant salvation. Only your faith in Jesus Christ does that. However, baptism is an outward sign of our inner commitment. It does not make you a believer in Christ; it shows that you already believe in Him and are committed to obeying Him.

Many people are insulted by God's command for water baptism, thinking it is silly and ridiculous. However, the Bible states otherwise. The act of baptism is a must for all who desire to follow Christ.

1) What was the circumcision a sign of under the old covenant? *(Genesis 17: 10 – 19)*

_____

_____

_____

2) What is the circumcision of Christ? *(Colossians 2:11-12)*

_____

_____

_____

3) How did Moses describe this true circumcision? *(Deuteronomy 30:6)*

_____

_____

_____

4) How did Peter respond to the question asked after his sermon? *(Acts 2:38)*

_____

_____

_____

5) What instructions did Jesus Christ leave for His Church? *(Matthew 28:19-20)*

_____

_____

_____

- **It's important to baptize believers in the name of the Father and of the Son, Jesus Christ, and of the Holy Spirit. Read Matthew 28:19; Acts 2:38; 8:14-16; 10:45-48; 19:5.**

> After forty years of wandering in the wilderness, the generation of disobedient Israelites died. When the Lord rolled back the waters of the Jordan River, this new generation walked through the river and into the Promised Land.
>
> Before the Israelites could possess the Promised Land, they had to be circumcised so that Egypt's reproach is rolled away from them. The circumcision was a sign of

their covenant with God. Under the new covenant, we must receive the circumcision of Jesus to put off the body of the sins of the flesh. Through baptism, we are uprooted from the world, and the reproach of the world is rolled away from us.

"We know that our old self [our human nature without the Holy Spirit] was nailed to the cross with *Him*, in order that our body of sin might be done away with, so that we would no longer be slaves to sin." (Romans 6:6, Amplified Version)

WATER BAPTISM IN THE OLD TESTAMENT

The Israelites were in bondage and enslaved to Pharaoh for many years. When the Lord brought them out of slavery in the Exodus, He parted the Red Sea. As the Israelites passed safely to the other side, the waters formed a wall on their right hand and their left. Pharaoh and his armies pursued the Israelites and followed them into the Red Sea. The Lord caused the waters to return and cover all the Pharaoh's army who came into the sea after them. Israel's children had walked on dry land in the midst of the sea, but all of the Egyptians were drowned, and not one remained. (Exodus 14)

Israel's oppressors, those who were pursuing her in her new relationship with God, were buried in the waters of the Red Sea. Israel was left alone on the other side of the water, free from slavery and free to be servants of their God. If the sea had not buried the Egyptians, the threat of slavery would have followed them into the Promised Land. Not only would Israel have had to fight her enemies in the Promised Land, but she would have had to fight the one who was trying to bring her back into bondage. Those who have come to faith in Christ and are identified with Him through water baptism have been made free from the power and bondage of sin. They pressed into the Promised Land and were able to meet and conquer their enemies head-on.

6) What does Paul say about Israel's experience at the Red Sea? *(1 Corinthians 10:1-2)*

_____

_____

_____

SESSION 6

100% of me belongs to Jesus, and He loves me. Song of Songs 7:10

7) Why did Jesus partake of our flesh, blood, and death? *(Hebrews 2:14-15)*

_____

_____

_____

8) How did the people respond when they received the Word of God? *(Acts 2:41)*

_____

_____

_____

9) What did the people of Samaria do after they believed Philip's teaching? *(Acts 8:12)*

_____

_____

_____

- **Notice the immediacy of all the baptisms recorded in the book of Acts. Likewise, there should be no delay in the baptism of believers today.**

10) What did the Ethiopian eunuch desire after he heard the message about the Messiah? *(Acts 8:35-36)*

_____

_____

_____

11) How was the eunuch baptized? *(Acts 8:38-39)*

_____

_____

_____

12) What happened to the Philippian jailer and his family after believing Paul's message? *(Acts 16:29 – 33)*

_____

_____

_____

13) How soon were the Philippian jailer and his family baptized? *(Acts 16:29 – 33)*

_____

_____

_____

14) Through baptism, what two experiences do believers share with Christ? *(Romans 6:4)*

_____

_____

_____

15) Since we are united with Him in the likeness of his death, what shall we also be? *(Romans 6:5)*

_____

_____

_____

16) Many believers have gone through the motions of baptism yet have not experienced a genuine New Testament baptism. What have they experienced? *(Acts 19:3-4)*

_____

_____

_____

When we read in Colossians 2:9 that "in Him, all the fullness of deity dwells in bodily form," Jesus' disciples understood this. They went everywhere baptizing new believers in His name. In the name of Jesus, demons are cast out, the sick are healed, and the lame walk.

Likewise, we must become as little children and obey the simple things that God commands us to do. His ways are far above our ways. We must not depend on our understanding. We must be careful lest we only desire to do incredible feats for God but are not willing to humble ourselves to God's way of doing things.

SESSION 6
PRAYER POINTS

100% of me belongs to Jesus, and He loves me. Song of Songs 7:10

- In the name of Jesus, Father, thank You for a new birth, a new heart, and for allowing Jesus to dwell in my heart.

- Thank you, Lord, for the opportunity to be baptized, immersed in water--buried and resurrected with You. Sin no longer has dominion over me. I declare I am a partaker of eternal life because eternal life is in Your Son, Jesus.

- Just as we see in Your word, I will share the good news about the Kingdom of God and the name of Jesus Christ for my friends and family to be saved.

RENUNCIATION

- I renounce all fear, rejection, and every other way to get to the Father.

SESSION 6

ANSWER KEY

1. Under the old covenant, circumcision was a sign of the covenant between God, Abraham, and his descendants. (Genesis 17:10-19)

2. The circumcision of Christ is putting off the body of the sins of the flesh and being buried with Him in baptism. (Colossians 2:11-12)

3. Moses described it as circumcision of the heart. (Deuteronomy 30:6)

4. Peter said, "Repent, and let every one of you be baptized in the name of Jesus Christ for the remission of sins; and you shall receive the gift of the Holy Spirit." (Acts 2:38)

5. Jesus said, "Go therefore and make disciples of all the nations, baptizing them in the name of the Father and of the Son and of the Holy Spirit, teaching them to observe all things that I have commanded you." (Matthew 28:19-20)

6. Paul says all were baptized into Moses in the sea. (1 Corinthians 10:1-2)

7. Through the death of Jesus, He destroyed the devil and released those who were subject to bondage. (Hebrews 2:14-15)

8. Those who gladly received his word were baptized. (Acts 2:41)

9. When they believed Philip as he preached the things concerning the Kingdom of God and the name of Jesus Christ, both men and women were baptized. (Acts 8:12)

10. He desired to be baptized. (Acts 8:35-36)

11. The eunuch went down into the water. (Acts 8:38-39)

12. He and all his family were immediately baptized. (Acts 16:29 – 33)

13. They were baptized immediately. (Acts 16:29 – 33)

14. We are buried with Him through baptism and raised from the dead. (Romans 6:4)

15. We shall also be in the likeness of His resurrection. (Romans 6:5)

16. They experienced the baptism of repentance. (Acts 19:3-4)

Baptism in the Holy Spirit.

7.

BAPTISM IN THE HOLY SPIRIT

The disciples were taught by and fellowshipped with Jesus for three years. They also saw the resurrected Christ in all His glory and power. However, they were not allowed to go and preach the Gospel until they received the baptism of the Holy Spirit. This empowerment produced the ability to be a witness; it gave the disciples the ability to preach the Gospel and live a Christian life. We, too, need the Holy Spirit to be a witness and disciple of Christ in the earth to preach the Gospel and live upright before the Lord.

1) What did Jesus tell His disciples to do before they went out into the world to preach repentance? *(Luke 24:47 – 49)*

_____

_____

_____

2) What was the "Promise of the Father" the disciples were to receive? *(Acts 1:4-5)*

_____

_____

_____

3) What did Jesus say would happen when the Holy Spirit came upon them? *(Acts 1:8)*

_____

_____

_____

THE HOLY SPIRIT COMES AT PENTECOST

4) Besides the 11 apostles, who else was waiting to receive the Holy Spirit's promise, and how many were present? *(Acts 1:13 – 15)*

_____

_____

_____

5) What happened when the Holy Spirit was given? *(Acts 2: 1-4)*

_____

_____

_____

6) What did the tongues of fire represent? *(Matthew 3:11)*

_____

_____

_____

7) Who was present in Jerusalem during the feast of Pentecost? *(Acts 2:5- 6)*

_____

_____

_____

8) What did Peter explain to them? *(Acts 2:14 – 21)*

_____

_____

_____

9) What instruction did Peter give to the people who were under conviction following his message at Pentecost? *(Acts 2:37 – 38)*

_____

_____

_____

HOLY SPIRIT

10) What did Jesus say about the Holy Spirit? *(John 14:16-17)*

_____

_____

_____

11) What are two names given for the Holy Spirit? *(John 14:16-17)*

_____

_____

_____

12) What other things did Jesus tell the disciples that the Holy Spirit would do for them? *(John 14:26, 15:26, 16:13)*

_____

_____

_____

13) What did Paul say about the Gospel that he preached? *(I Corinthians 2:4)*

_____

_____

_____

14) Where did Paul say the faith of men should rest? *(I Corinthians 2:5)*

_____

_____

_____

15) How did Paul say that we might know the things God has given us? *(I Corinthians 2:9-12)*

_____

_____

_____

16) What did Jesus say the Spirit would do for us when we are delivered up before the governors, kings, and those in authority? *(Matthew 10:18-20)*

_____

_____

_____

17) What are we encouraged to do when we are delivered up for the defense of the Gospel? *(Matthew 10:19)*

_____

_____

_____

18) How did Jesus fulfill his ministry? *(Acts 10:38)*

_____

_____

_____

100% of me belongs to Jesus, and He loves me. Song of Songs 7:10

CLEANSING AND PURIFYING WORK OF THE HOLY SPIRIT

> The fire of the Holy Spirit represents the cleansing and purifying work of the Spirit in believers' lives. This work of the Holy Spirit does not take place overnight. It is a process like that of a smelter or a refiner of silver. The refiner heats the silver over a fire, and as the silver becomes hot, the dross and impurities rise to the top. He skims the impurities off and repeats the process until he sees his image reflected clearly in the silver. In the same way, the Holy Spirit skims the dross and impurities from our lives through the process of discipleship, testing, and trials so that Jesus may be seen in us.

19) Describe the refining and purifying work that the Holy Spirit does. *(Malachi 3:1 – 3)*

_____

_____

_____

20) What does Paul say the Spirit of the Lord has come to do? *(II Corinthians 3:18)*

_____

_____

_____

RECEIVING THE HOLY SPIRIT

21) How did the believers in Samaria receive the Holy Spirit? *(Acts 8:17)*

_____

_____

_____

22) How did the believers in Ephesus receive the Holy Spirit, and what happened when the Holy Spirit came upon them? *(Acts 19:6)*

_____

_____

_____

SESSION 7

23) How did the Gentiles receive the Holy Spirit? *(Acts 10:44-46)*

_____

_____

_____

24) How did those present know the Gentiles had received the Holy Spirit? *(Acts 10:45-46)*

_____

_____

_____

25) What does the prophet Ezekiel say about the Holy Spirit when he is prophesying about the new covenant? *(Ezekiel 36:26 – 27)*

_____

_____

_____

26) To whom is the promised gift of the Holy Spirit made available? *(Acts 2:39)*

_____

_____

_____

27) To whom will the Father give the Holy Spirit? *(Luke 11:13)*

_____

_____

_____

- **The fire of the Holy Spirit represents the cleansing and purifying work of the Spirit in believers' lives.**

PRAYER POINTS

- **Thank you, Lord, for sending the Holy Spirit as a Helper, Comforter, and Spirit of truth to dwell with me and in me.**

- ***If you have not yet received the promise of the Holy Spirit:*** Father, You are the giver of every good and perfect gift, and Your Word says that You will give the Holy Spirit to all Your children who ask You. I desire Your Holy Spirit that I may be empowered to preach the Gospel and follow Christ, and I'm asking today to receive the promise of the Holy Spirit with the evidence of tongues.

- Holy Spirit, thank You for Your refining work in my life. When I am struggling, please remind me that you are skimming the impurities from my life so I may be a new creature formed in the image of Christ.

RENUNCIATIONS

- I renounce all fear, unbelief, and doubt.

- I renounce self-will and arrogance.

ANSWER KEY

1. Jesus said to His disciples, "I send the Promise of My Father upon you; but tarry in the city of Jerusalem until you are endued with power from on high." (Luke 24:47-49)

2. The disciples were to receive the baptism of the Holy Spirit. (Acts 1:4-5)

3. Jesus said they would receive power to be His witnesses. (Acts 1:8)

4. The disciples were waiting with the women, Mary, the mother of Jesus, and His brothers. There were about 120 people present in the upper room. (Acts 1:13 – 15)

5. There came from heaven a noise like a violent rushing wind that filled the whole house. Tongues of fire appeared before them and sat upon each of them, and they began to speak with other tongues as the Spirit gave them utterance. (Acts 2: 1-4)

6. The tongues of fire represented the baptism of fire. (Matthew 3:11)

7. Jews from every nation were present in Jerusalem. (Acts 2:5- 6)

8. Peter explained that this was the outpouring of the Holy Spirit spoken of by the prophet Joel. (Acts 2:14 – 21)

9. Peter told the people to repent, be baptized, and receive the Holy Spirit. (Acts 2:37 – 38)

10. Jesus said that the Holy Spirit "dwells with you and will be in you." (John 14:16-17)

11. The Scriptures name the Holy Spirit a Helper, or Comforter, and the Spirit of truth. (John 14:16-17)

12. Jesus said the Holy Spirit would teach you all things and bring to your remembrance all the things that Jesus said. The Holy Spirit will also testify of Jesus, guide you into all truth, and tell you things to come. (John 14:26, 15:26, 16:13)

13. Paul said of the Gospel he preached, "my speech and my preaching were not with persuasive words of human wisdom, but in demonstration of the Spirit and of power." (I Corinthians 2:4)

14. Paul said the faith of men should rest in the power of God, not in the wisdom of men. (I Corinthians 2:5)

15. Paul said that we would know the things of God by the revelation of the Spirit, which is in us. (I Corinthians 2:9 – 12)

16. Jesus said, "For it will be given to you in that hour what you should speak; for it is not you who speak, but the Spirit of your Father who speaks in you." (Matthew 10:18-20)

17. We are encouraged not to worry about how or what we should speak. (Matthew 10:19)

18. Jesus fulfilled His ministry through the anointing of the Holy Spirit. (Acts 10:38)

19. The Holy Spirit is like a launderer's soap and a refiner's fire. He will purge and purify believers, that they may offer the Lord an offering of righteousness. (Malachi 3:1-3)

SESSION 7

100% of me belongs to Jesus, and He loves me. Song of Songs 7:10

20. Paul said that the Spirit has come to transform us into the image of the Lord from glory to glory. (II Corinthians 3:18)

21. The believers in Samaria received the Holy Spirit through the laying on of hands. (Acts 8:17)

22. The believers at Ephesus received the Holy Spirit through the laying of hands, and they spoke in tongues and prophesied. (Acts 19:6)

23. The Holy Spirit fell on the Gentiles as they heard Peter's preaching. (Acts 10:44-46)

24. Those present knew the Gentiles had received the Holy Spirit because they heard them speak with tongues and magnify God. (Acts 10:45-46)

25. The prophet Ezekiel prophesied that God would put a new Spirit in us and cause us to walk in His statutes. (Ezekiel 36:26 – 27)

26. The promise of the Holy Spirit is "to you and your children, and to all who are afar off, as many as the Lord our God will call." (Acts 2:39)

27. The Father will give the Holy Spirit to all His children who ask Him. (Luke 11:13)

The Mission and the Church.

8.

THE MISSION AND THE CHURCH

Every Christian has the same mission. Jesus Christ was clear about what He left His Church on the earth to do and how He expects the people who follow Him to live. Sound reasoning should lead any Christian to believe that Jesus is the best leader, with the best vision and the best know-how concerning His Kingdom and the people He died for, including you.

OUR MISSION

To become laid down lovers of God, servant lovers of all - one at a time, and make disciples who will do the same in every community, state, region, and nation.

1) According to Jesus, what is the first and greatest commandment? *(Matthew 22:36-38)*

_____

_____

_____

2) According to Jesus, what is the second greatest commandment? *(Matthew 22:39)*

_____

_____

_____

- **Our mission is the great commandment and the great commission expressed in one statement. Who better to point the Church's direction than the Head of the Church, Jesus Christ Himself.**

3) How much of the law and the prophets would a person fulfill if they do these two things? *(Matthew 22:40)*

_____

_____

_____

4) In the parable of the good Samaritan, what did the lawyer ask Jesus? *(Luke 10:25)*

_____

_____

_____

5) What was Jesus' response to the lawyer when he answered with the first and second commandments? *(Luke 10:26-28)*

_____

_____

_____

6) What is the first instruction given in this scripture? *(Matthew 28:19-20)*

_____

_____

_____

7) What instructions did Jesus Christ leave for His Church? *(Matthew 28:19-20)*

_____

_____

_____

8) Where did Jesus direct us to go, and what did He direct us to do? *(Mark 16:15)*

_____

_____

_____

9) According to Jesus, who will be saved? *(Mark 16:16)*

_____

_____

_____

10) After the disciples received the Holy Spirit, where did Jesus say they would first be witnesses of Him? *(Acts 1:8)*

_____

_____

_____

11) What does Jerusalem represent? *(Acts 1:8)*

_____

_____

_____

> As disciples, we preach the Gospel and baptize those who believe. After that, the work of making them a disciple and teaching them to obey begins.

WHAT IS THE CHURCH?

Ekklesia is the Greek word that has been translated into "church" in the New Testament more than 100 times. *Ekklesia* means a company of people chosen and called. The proper translation, which was abandoned for political reasons, is Assembly. The Assembly is the congregation of baptized believers united by covenant to affect the will of the Lord Jesus Christ in its given locality.

The New Testament examples of the church are vastly different from the contemporary notion of where members go, usually once a week. Back then, the Assembly was used to describe a group of people, never a building. Furthermore, the early Church was a transforming organism, not a static institution. Read Acts 2:46-47, 5:42.

12) Who is the founder and builder of the Church? *(Matthew 16:18)*

_____

_____

_____

13) Is Jesus Christ also the head of the church? *(Colossians 1:18)*

_____

_____

_____

14) Who is the body of Christ? *(Colossians 1:24)*

_____

_____

_____

15) What makes up the body of Christ? *(Romans 12:4-5; 1 Corinthians 12:12-14)*

_____

_____

_____

SESSION 8

100% of me belongs to Jesus, and He loves me. Song of Songs 7:10

16) What are we, and what are we being made into? *(1 Peter 2:5)*

_____

_____

_____

17) How is the church described in this scripture? *(1 Peter 2:9-10)*

_____

_____

_____

> When a group of two or three Roman citizens gathered anywhere in the world, it constituted the conventus as Rome's local expression. Even though geography separated them from the capital of the empire, their coming together as fellow citizens automatically brought Rome's power and presence into their midst. We do the same as Christians coming together in Jesus' Name.
>
> Read Matthew 18:20.

HOMEWORK

> Read the mission aloud and then write it out using the space below. You will also rewrite the mission for homework in the back of the book.
>
> ### THE MISSION
>
> *To become laid down lovers of God, servant lovers of all - one at a time, and make disciples who will do the same in every community, state, region, and nation.*

PRAYER POINTS

- I will become a laid down lover of God, servant lover of all-one at a time, and make disciples who will do the same in every community, state, region, and nation.

- Father, make me bold as a lion as I go out into all the world to preach the Gospel!

- I declare I will be a faithful witness who delivers souls.

- I pray I will make disciples who glorify You!

RENUNCIATION

- I renounce faith without works and self-preservation.

SESSION 8

100% of me belongs to Jesus, and He loves me. Song of Songs 7:10

ANSWER KEY

1. Jesus said the first and great commandment is, "You shall love the Lord your God with all your heart, with all your soul, and with all your mind." (Matthew 22:36-38)

2. Jesus said, "You shall love your neighbor as yourself." (Matthew 22:39)

3. If a person does these two things, they will fulfill all the Law and the Prophets. (Matthew 22:40)

4. The man asks Jesus, "what shall I do to inherit eternal life?" (Luke 10:25)

5. Jesus said to him, "You have answered rightly; do this, and you will live." (Luke 10:26-28)

6. The first instruction given is to "go." (Matthew 28:19-20)

7. Jesus said, "Go therefore and make disciples of all the nations, baptizing them in the name of the Father and of the Son and the Holy Spirit, teaching them to observe all things that I have commanded you." (Matthew 28:19-20)

8. Jesus said, "Go into all the world and preach the gospel to every creature." (Mark 16:15)

9. He who believes and is baptized will be saved. (Mark 16:16)

10. Jesus said to start in Jerusalem. (Acts 1:8)

11. Jerusalem represents the place you live. (Acts 1:8)

12. Jesus is the founder and builder of His Church. (Matthew 16:18)

13. Yes. Jesus Christ is the head of the body, the church. (Colossians 1:18)

14. The Church is the body of Christ. (Colossians 1:24)

15. We are one body with many members. (Romans 12:4-5; 1 Corinthians 12:12-14)

16. We are living stones and are being built up a spiritual house, a holy priesthood. (1 Peter 2:5)

17. The church is described as "a chosen generation, a royal priesthood, a holy nation, His own special people." (1 Peter 2:9-10)

Financial Principles.

SESSION

9.

9.

FINANCIAL PRINCIPLES

There are an enormous amount of passages in the Bible that deal with the subject of money. Money is a powerful tool that, like most things, can be used either for great good or great evil. We will explore the dangers and opportunities that money presents to a follower of Jesus. We will also examine our attitude towards money to see if we view money as a means to an end or as an end in itself.

BIBLICAL PRINCIPLES OF PROSPERITY

Just because something is dangerous does not mean we should never use it. For example, cars are unsafe, but that does not mean we should stop driving and walk everywhere. Instead, we need to obey the traffic rules for our safety. Similarly, the proper response to the dangers of money is not to be intentionally impoverished but to handle the money God gives us according to His principles. We must carefully consider how we will steward what the Lord provides, whether large or small.

1) Who gives us the ability to produce wealth? *(Deuteronomy 8:18)*

_____

_____

_____

2) What was promised to Israel if they obeyed God's commands? *(Deuteronomy 30:8-9)*

_____

_____

_____

3) What happens when we give? *(Luke 6:38)*

_____

_____

_____

4) How does the law of sowing and reaping apply to money? *(2 Corinthians 9:6)*

_____

_____

_____

5) What is God able to do for the cheerful giver? *(2 Corinthians 9:7-8)*

_____

_____

_____

6) Why does God provide riches for His people? *(2 Corinthians 9:11)*

_____

_____

_____

Personal Reflection: How has God blessed me with abundance? How can I use that abundance to bless others?

SESSION 9

100% of me belongs to Jesus, and He loves me. Song of Songs 7:10

PUTTING GOD FIRST

7) What did Abraham do in response to the blessing of God? *(Genesis 14:18-20)*

_____

_____

- **Some will say Abraham only offered a tithe one time when, in fact, it is only written once. It is recorded that Jesus prayed less than seven times in the Bible. Do you think He prayed less than seven times, or do you think it was a part of His life before the Father?**

8) If you belong to Christ, how are you related to Abraham, and what will you do? *(Galatians 3:29, John 8:39)*

_____

_____

_____

9) What part should we give to God? *(Proverbs 3:9)*

_____

_____

_____

10) How is the tithe described? How much of the increase goes to God? *(Leviticus 27:30-32)*

_____

_____

_____

11) Should the tithe be an afterthought or forethought, and what will happen if you give the first part to God? *(Proverbs 3:9-10)*

_____

_____

_____

God has given us the command of tithing as a blessing. Many refuse the blessing with various excuses, including financial struggle, lack of understanding, etc. However, whether we tithe or not comes down to what has captured your heart: you, your situation, or Jesus.

Many people give beyond the ten percent (tithe) but have great difficulty submitting to the tithe as something God requires. This attitude exposes a significant flaw in a person's character called lawlessness. Those who are lawless may not have a problem with giving, but they have a problem being told to give. Remember, it is possible to stand with Christ in confession and doctrine while standing with satan in principle and practice.

Personal Reflection: Does this apply to you? What did you learn from the Scriptures, and how will you use it in your life?

THE DANGERS OF WEALTH

The Apostle Paul wrote that he had learned how to be content with both poverty and abundance. Read Philippians 4:12-13. Jesus also had rich friends who helped support Him (Luke 8:3). Wealth, according to the Bible, is good but dangerous. Everyone knows the good that money can bring, but the Bible is clear about its temptations also:

- Desire riches (1 Timothy 6:10)

- Worry about money (Matthew 6:25-34)

- Trust in wealth rather than God (Luke 12:16-21, Mark 4:18-19)

- Love and serve money as your god (Matthew 6:24)

- Use your money to oppress others (James 2:6, Isaiah 3:15, Amos 2:6-7)

Wise men fear the temptations that wealth brings.

SESSION 9

100% of me belongs to Jesus, and He loves me. Song of Songs 7:10

12) According to Jesus' parable of the sower, what can choke out God's Word and cause it to be unfruitful? *(Mark 4:18 – 19)*

_____

_____

_____

13) What are some of the worries of life that choke out God's Word? *(Matthew 6:25, 28, 31, 34)*

_____

_____

_____

14) What should we guard ourselves against? *(Luke 12:15)*

_____

_____

_____

15) For the love of _____ is a root of all kinds of evil. *(1 Timothy 6:10)*

16) It is impossible to serve both God and _____. *(Luke 16:13)*

17) Jesus never made such a statement about anything else. Why not?

_____

_____

_____

18) What can happen to those who are eager for money and want to get rich? *(1 Timothy 6:9– 10)*

_____

_____

_____

19) What can deliver us from death: righteousness or money? *(Proverbs 11:4)*

_____

_____

_____

20) What happens to the one who trusts in money? *(Proverbs 11:28)*

_____

_____

_____

21) What is the point of the parable of the rich fool? *(Luke 12:16 – 21)*

_____

_____

_____

22) Where is your heart? *(Matthew 6:19-21)*

_____

_____

_____

Personal Reflection: What did you learn about the dangers of money?

EXTREME GENEROSITY

Some people spend all they can afford to spend, and they are always broke. Some spend less, and they continually save their money. Others spend more than they have and are in debt. Some give less than they are able and required, and this is disobedience. Others give what they are able and directed, and this is obedience. Some sacrificially give beyond their ability and requirement. These extreme givers, like the widow in the temple, are considered heroes of the faith.

23) According to Jesus, who gave the most and why? *(Luke 21:1- 4)*

_____

_____

_____

24) How much did the Macedonians give? *(2 Corinthians 8: 3)*

_____

_____

_____

25) Did Paul have to pressure the Macedonian believers to give? *(2 Corinthians 8:4)*

_____

_____

_____

PERSONAL REFLECTION:

26) What kind of giver are you?

_____

_____

_____

27) Are you a faithful and grateful person who tithes?

_____

_____

_____

28) Are you a person who gives with the right heart?

_____

_____

_____

29) What changes must you make immediately?

_____

_____

_____

As Christians, we give our tithes to the church we attend. We also give to our leaders and support different ministry initiatives as led by the Holy Spirit.

HOMEWORK

Read the mission aloud, and then fill in the blanks below. You will also write out the entire mission for homework in the back of the book.

> ### THE MISSION
> To become _____ _____ _____ of God, _____ lovers of all
> _____ _____ _____ _____, and _____ _____ who
> will do the _____ in every _____, _____, region and _____

PRAYER POINTS

- Lord, I thank You for the power to get wealth to establish Your covenant. I thank You that the blessing of Abraham is my portion.

- I will be a faithful tither and cheerful giver.

- Father, help me not to be deceived by riches.

- Father, I thank You for providing all of my needs according to Your riches in glory by Christ.

RENUNCIATION

- I renounce the love of money and covetousness.

ANSWER KEY

1. God gives the ability to obtain wealth. (Deuteronomy 8:18)

2. If Israel obeyed, the Lord promised to make them abound in all the work of their hand, in the fruit of their body, in the increase of their livestock, and the produce of their land for good. (Deuteronomy 30:8-9)

3. With the same measure that we give, it will be measured back to us. (Luke 6:38)

4. He who sows sparingly will reap sparingly, and he who sows bountifully will also reap bountifully. (2 Corinthians 9:6)

5. God can make all grace abound towards the cheerful giver. (2 Corinthians 9:7-8)

6. God provides riches for His people so they may give generously, and those who are blessed by this generosity may give thanksgiving to God. (2 Corinthians 9:11)

7. Abraham gave a tithe of all. (Genesis 14:18-20)

8. We are Abraham's seed, and we will do the works of Abraham. (Galatians 3:29, John 8:39)

9. We should give God the first part of our increase. (Proverbs 3:9)

10. The tithe is described as holy, and a tenth of the increase goes to God. (Leviticus 27:30-32)

11. The tithe must be a forethought. Your barns will be filled with plenty, and your vats will overflow with new wine. (Proverbs 3:9-10)

12. According to Jesus, the cares of this world, the deceitfulness of riches, and the desires for other things entering in can choke out God's Word and cause it to be unfruitful. (Mark 4:18 – 19)

13. God's Word can be choked out with worries about your life, body, food, drink, clothing, and tomorrow. (Matthew 6:25, 28, 31, 34)

14. Jesus said we should guard against covetousness. (Luke 12:15)

15. The love of money is a root of all kinds of evil. (1 Timothy 6:10)

16. It is impossible to serve both God and Mammon. (Luke 16:13)

17. Only Mammon can masquerade as God and answer all things until death.

18. Their desire to be rich can cause them to stray from the faith and pierce them through with many sorrows. (1 Timothy 6:9– 10)

19. Righteousness can deliver us from death. (Proverbs 11:4)

20. He who trusts in his riches will fall. (Proverbs 11:28)

21. The parable of the rich fool demonstrates that it is foolish to store up earthly treasure instead of heavenly treasure. Our time on earth is limited, and we don't know when God will call us. (Luke 12:16 – 21)

22. According to the scripture, your heart will be with your treasure. (Matthew 6:19-21)

23. The poor widow gave the most because she was not wealthy, and she gave all the livelihood that she had. (Luke 21:1- 4)

24. The Macedonians gave freely, according to and beyond their abilities. (2 Corinthians 8:3)

25. Paul did not have to pressure the Macedonian believers to give. Instead, they implored Paul with much urgency to receive their gift. (2 Corinthians 8:4)

The Lifestyle of a Disciple of Jesus Christ.
Part 1.

10.

THE LIFESTYLE OF A DISCIPLE OF JESUS CHRIST

PART 1

As Christians, times in our lives are intensified by both the enemy's opposition and the transforming work of the Holy Spirit. It could easily seem that everything is working against you. These seasons bring to the forefront our weaknesses and our strengths. If we can recognize different seasons in life, we can better deal with them and avoid discouragement and overconfidence. During these times, many walk away from the faith due to the deceitfulness of sin, unbelief, and discouragement.

UNBELIEF

Read Hebrews 3:12-13 to answer the following questions.

1) What is the nature of sin? *(v. 13)*

_____

_____

_____

2) What will sin do to the person through its deceitfulness? *(v. 13)*

_____

_____

_____

3) Is it possible for a believer to depart from the living God? *(v. 12)*

_____

_____

_____

4) Why must a person guard themselves against this deception? *(v. 12)*

_____

_____

_____

5) What causes the brethren to depart from the living God? *(v. 12)*

_____

_____

_____

6) Who is responsible for keeping us away from being deceived and becoming hard-hearted? *(v. 12)*

_____

_____

_____

SESSION 10

100% of me belongs to Jesus, and He loves me. Song of Songs 7:10

7) Without the brethren, can one avoid the deception of sin?

_____

_____

_____

- **A bitter soul is a soul that refuses to be broken.**

SEEK GOD AND PRESS FORWARD

8) What happens when we search for God? *(Jeremiah 29:13)*

_____

_____

_____

9) What happens if we forsake Him? *(1 Chronicles 28:9)*

_____

_____

_____

10) What happens when our mind is not on things above but on the places which we came from and worldly experiences we have had? *(Hebrews 11:13-16)*

_____

_____

_____

11) Brethren, I do not count myself to have apprehended; but one thing I do, _____ those things which are _____ and _____ to those things which are _____, I _____ the _____ for the _____ of the upward call of God in Christ Jesus. *(Philippians 3:13-14)*

OUR ATTITUDE

12) Does a good soldier, engaged in warfare, entangle himself in the affairs of life? *(2 Timothy 2:4)*

_____

_____

_____

13) Why doesn't a good soldier engage himself in the affairs of life? *(2 Timothy 2:4)*

_____

_____

_____

- **When we are not entangled in the affairs of life, it has minimal influence over our attitude.**

14) What should our attitude be towards the affiliations and sufferings we experience in life? *(2 Corinthians 4:17; Romans 8:18)*

_____

_____

_____

FASTING

Throughout the Bible, people fasted in repentance, mourning, and a desire for God. Today, we fast for all those reasons in addition to longing for Jesus. We have the promise of being able to deal with more stubborn situations and demons as well.

15) What did Jesus say His disciples would do? *(Matthew 9:15)*

_____

_____

_____

SESSION 10

100% of me belongs to Jesus, and He loves me. Song of Songs 7:10

16) While Jesus was walking with His disciples, why didn't they fast? *(Mark 2:20)*

_____

_____

_____

17) According to Jesus, what would lead His disciples to fast? *(Luke 5:35)*

_____

_____

_____

18) Along with their faith, what else did Jesus say was needed for the young boy to be free? *(Matthew 17:20-21)*

_____

_____

_____

HOMEWORK

> Share the mission aloud with your partnering disciple, and then write it out using the space below. You will also rewrite the mission for homework in the back of the book.

PRAYER POINTS

- **Lord, I pray I will go from faith to faith and from glory to glory! Purge all unbelief out of my heart.**

- **Give me a heart of flesh to endure the seasons of testing in my life.**

- **I pray I would have the mind of Christ--being mindful of the things of God and not of men.**

- **As I walk after the Spirit, let fasting and praying to be a continual part of my life as a disciple of Jesus Christ.**

ANSWER KEY

1. Sin is deceitful. (Hebrews 3:13)

2. The deceitfulness of sin will harden a person. (Hebrews 3:13)

3. Yes, a believer can depart from the living God. (Hebrews 3:12)

4. A person must guard themselves against unbelief, or their heart will become evil. (Hebrews 3:12)

5. An evil heart of unbelief causes the brethren to depart from the living God. (Hebrews 3:12)

6. The brethren, our brothers and sisters in Christ, are responsible for keeping us from being deceived and hard-hearted. (Hebrews 3:12)

7. Without the brethren, you cannot avoid the deception of sin.

8. When we search for God with all of our hearts, we will find Him. (Jeremiah 29:13)

9. If we forsake Him, He will cast us off forever. (1 Chronicles 28:9)

10. When you call to mind the place from which you had come out, you would desire the opportunity to return. (Hebrews 11:13-16)

11. Brethren, I do not count myself to have apprehended; but one thing I do, forgetting those things which are behind and reaching forward to those things which are ahead, I press toward the goal for the prize of the upward call of God in Christ Jesus. (Philippians 3:13-14)

12. No one engaged in warfare entangles himself with the affairs of this life. (2 Timothy 2:4)

13. A good soldier does not entangle himself with the affairs of life to please Him who enlisted him as a soldier. (2 Timothy 2:4)

14. Our affiliations are light and momentarily, and the sufferings of this present time are not worthy of being compared with the glory which shall be revealed in us. (2 Corinthians 4:17; Romans 8:18)

15. Jesus said His disciples would fast. (Matthew 9:15)

16. Jesus said His disciples did not fast because the bridegroom was still with them. (Mark 2:20)

17. Jesus said, "But the days will come when the bridegroom shall be taken away from them; then they will fast in those days." Their desire to be close to Jesus would lead them to fast. (Luke 5:35)

18. Jesus said prayer and fasting were also needed. (Matthew 17:20-21)

The Lifestyle of a Disciple of Jesus Christ.
Part 2.

11.

THE LIFESTYLE OF A DISCIPLE OF JESUS CHRIST

Part 2

Your life as a disciple will be radically different than what it was before. Inside you are new, and outside will put God's work on display. Your time will be spent focusing on the most important things to God and His plans for you on earth. Throughout the word of God, there are disclosures about the likes and dislikes of God. Our behavior must be in line with the work that God has done in us. Old habits can be hard to break, but your new discipline and commitment to living for God will make the process as seamless as can be. Below you will find a few things that should be considered "low hanging fruit" that can be addressed immediately. Be encouraged, God is on your side, and you have the Holy Spirit!

SPEECH

1) What does the Bible say about swearing falsely (vows) and oaths? *(Matthew 5:33 – 36)*

_____

_____

_____

2) How are we to respond to certain questions, and why? *(Matthew 5:37)*

_____

_____

_____

3) For out of the abundance of the heart _____. *(Matthew 12:34-35)*

_____

_____

_____

4) What will happen to us for speaking idle words? *(Matthew 12:36)*

_____

_____

_____

5) How shall we be justified, and how shall we be condemned? *(Matthew 12:37)*

_____

_____

_____

6) A _____ answer turns away wrath, but a _____ word stirs up anger. *(Proverbs 15:1)*

7) The words of a man's mouth are _____ waters; the wellspring of _____ is a _____. *(Proverbs 18:4)*

100% of me belongs to Jesus, and He loves me. Song of Songs 7:10

PERSECUTION

8) When we are persecuted for the sake of Christ and His Kingdom, how should we respond? *(Matthew 5:10 – 12)*

_____

_____

_____

9) Read Matthew 5:22 and see what Jesus says about murder in the heart. "But I say to you that whoever is _____ with his _____ shall be in danger of the _____. And whoever says to his brother, _____ shall be in danger of the _____. But whoever says, _____ shall be in danger of _____".

- Raca means "empty-headed" or "good for nothing." It was an offensive term. When reading Matthew 5:22, the simple fact is that words kill.

10) What should your attitude be toward one who mistreats or slaps you? *(Matthew 5:39)*

_____

_____

_____

11) While some have said it is okay to hate your enemies, what does Jesus say? *(Matthew 5:43-47)*

_____

_____

_____

12) How does God demonstrate this type of love? *(Matthew 5:45)*

_____

_____

_____

13) If you love only those who love you, is that any credit to you? *(Luke 6:32 – 33)*

_____

_____

_____

14) _____, and you shall not be judged. Condemn not, and you shall _____. Forgive, and you _____. *(Luke 6:37)*

15) Amid persecution, how did Jesus respond? *(1 Peter 2:23)*

_____

_____

_____

FORGIVENESS

16) How often are you to forgive others? *(Matthew 18:21 – 22)*

_____

_____

_____

17) If you present your offering to God and remember your brother has something against you, what are you to do? *(Matthew 5:23 – 24)*

_____

_____

_____

18) If you do not forgive others, what attitude does the Father take toward you? *(Matthew 6:14 – 15)*

_____

_____

_____

19) How are you to treat others? *(Matthew 7:12; Luke 6:31)*

_____

_____

_____

100% of me belongs to Jesus, and He loves me. Song of Songs 7:10

HUMILITY

20) What does Jesus teach us about humility? *(Luke 18:10 – 14)*

_____

_____

_____

21) When _____ comes, then comes shame; But with the _____ is wisdom. *(Proverbs 11:2)*

22) Likewise you younger people, _____ yourselves to·your elders. Yes, all of you be submissive to one another, and be clothed with _____, for "God _____ the proud, But gives _____ to the humble." *(1 Peter 5:5)*

23) If you desire to be great and first in the Kingdom, what posture should you take before others? *(Matthew 20:26 – 28)*

_____

_____

_____

SIGNS OF LOVE

24) What is the greatest sign of love? *(John 15:13)*

_____

_____

_____

25) What should be your attitude toward giving to others? *(Luke 6:29 – 30, 34 – 35)*

_____

_____

_____

26) What did Jesus say for us to do if we love him? *(John 21:15 – 17)* ·

_____

_____

_____

27) How are we expected to show love to the brethren in need? *(Matthew 25:35 – 40)*

_____

_____

_____

28) How are we expected to love one another? *(1 John 3:16 – 18)*

_____

_____

_____

FAITHFULNESS

29) What did Jesus say about faithfulness? *(Luke 16:10)*

_____

_____

_____

30) What did Jesus say about the unjust? *(Luke 16:10)*

_____

_____

_____

31) Who did Apostle Paul say to commit the work? *(2 Timothy 2:2)*

_____

_____

_____

HOMEWORK

Share the mission aloud with your partnering disciple, and then write it out using the space below. You will also rewrite the mission for homework in the back of the book.

SESSION 11

100% of me belongs to Jesus, and He loves me. Song of Songs 7:10

PRAYER POINTS

- Lord, let the words of my mouth and meditation of my heart be acceptable to You. Help me to cleanse myself from all filthiness of the flesh and Spirit. Let my "yes" be "yes" and "no" be "no."

- Father, You have forgiven me, and I will forgive others.

- Father, help me to love the brethren in deed and truth

ANSWER KEY

1. We should not swear falsely or make an oath. (Matthew 5:33 – 36)

2. Our 'Yes' should be 'Yes,' and our 'No' should be 'No.' For whatever is more than these is from the evil one. (Matthew 5:37)

3. For out of the abundance of the heart, the mouth speaks. (Matthew 12:34-35)

4. We will give account for every word on the day of judgment. (Matthew 12:36)

5. By our words, we will be justified, and by our words, we will be condemned. (Matthew 12:37)

6. A soft answer turns away wrath, but a harsh word stirs up anger. (Proverbs 15:1)

7. The words of a man's mouth are deep waters; The wellspring of wisdom is a flowing brook. (Proverbs 18:4)

8. When we are persecuted, we should consider ourselves blessed, rejoice, and be exceedingly glad. (Matthew 5:10 – 12)

9. But I say to you that whoever is angry with his brother without a cause shall be in danger of the judgment. And whoever says to his brother, 'Raca!' shall be in danger of the council. But whoever says, 'You fool!' shall be in danger of hell fire. (Matthew 5:22)

10. Whoever slaps you on your right cheek, turn the other to him also. (Matthew 5:39)

11. Jesus says we need to love our enemies, bless those who curse us, do good to those who hate us, and pray for those who spitefully use us and persecute us. (Matthew 5:43-47)

12. He makes His sun rise on the evil and the good and sends rain on the just and the unjust. (Matthew 5:45)

13. No. For even sinners love those who love them. (Luke 6:32 – 33)

14. Judge not, and you shall not be judged. Condemn not, and you shall not be condemned. Forgive, and you will be forgiven. (Luke 6:37)

15. When Jesus was reviled and suffered, he did not revile or threaten in return. He committed Himself to Him who judges righteously. (1 Peter 2:23)

16. Jesus said we are to forgive others up to seventy times seven. (Matthew 18:21 – 22)

17. We should leave our gift there before the altar and be reconciled to our brother. Then we can come and offer our gift to God. (Matthew 5:23 – 24)

18. If you do not forgive men, neither will your Father forgive your trespasses. (Matthew 6:14 – 15)

19. Whatever you want men to do to you, do also to them. (Matthew 7:12; Luke 6:31)

20. Jesus says, "for everyone who exalts himself will be humbled, and he who humbles himself will be exalted." (Luke 18:10 – 14)

SESSION 11

100% of me belongs to Jesus, and He loves me. Song of Songs 7:10

21. When pride comes, then comes shame; But with the humble is wisdom. (Proverbs 11:2)

22. Likewise, you younger people, submit yourselves to your elders. Yes, all of you be submissive to one another, and be clothed with humility, for "God resists the proud, But gives grace to the humble." (1 Peter 5:5)

23. Whoever desires to become great and first shall be a servant and slave. (Matthew 20:26 – 28)

24. Jesus says to lay down one's life for his friends is the greatest sign of love. (John 15:13)

25. According to the scripture-- (Luke 6:29 – 30, 34 – 35)

26. Whoever takes your cloak, give him your tunic also.

27. Whoever takes what is yours, do not demand it back.

28. Love your enemies, do good, and lend, hoping for nothing in return.

29. If we love Jesus, we will feed His lambs and tend to His sheep. (John 21:15 – 17)

30. Among the brethren, we are expected to feed the hungry, give water to the thirsty, take in the stranger, clothe the naked, and visit the sick and those in prison. (Matthew 25:35 – 40)

31. We are expected to love one another in deed and truth, not in word or in tongue. (1 John 3:16 – 18)

32. Jesus says, "He who is faithful in what is least is faithful also in much." (Luke 16:10)

33. Jesus says, "he who is unjust in what is least is unjust also in much." (Luke 16:10)

34. Apostle Paul says, "commit these to faithful men who will be able to teach others also." (2 Timothy 2:2)

Commitment to the Body of Christ.

12.

COMMITMENT TO THE BODY OF CHRIST

According to the New Testament, those who have repented of sin and turned from the world's ways are the true believers that make up the Assembly of Jesus. They bring forth fruit as they are joined together into a local expression of Christ on earth. The body of Christ is not a building with a steeple on top. It is a living, active organism of which you are a part.

1) What makes up the body of Christ? *(Romans 12: 4-5; 1 Corinthians 12:12-14)*

_____

_____

_____

2) As children of God, what were we baptized into? *(1 Corinthians 12:13-14)*

_____

_____

_____

3) What are we, and what are we corporately being built into? *(1 Peter 2:5, Ephesians 2:21-22)*

_____

_____

_____

4) How did Jesus say we are to love one another? *(John 13:34)*

_____

_____

_____

5) By what sign did Jesus say all men would know we are His disciples? *(John 13:35)*

_____

_____

_____

6) In defining that love, what do the scriptures say? *(1 John 3:16, John 15:13)*

_____

_____

_____

7) This love also expresses itself in commitment to each other in the following ways:

    a) (1 Peter 4:8)

_____

_____

_____

SESSION 12

100% of me belongs to Jesus, and He loves me. Song of Songs 7:10

b) (Galatians 5:15)

_____

_____

c) (Philippians 2:3-4)

_____

_____

d) (1 Corinthians 12:26, Romans 15:1)

_____

_____

_____

e) (Matthew 5:44)

_____

_____

_____

f) (James 5:16, 1 Corinthians 12:25)

_____

_____

_____

g) (1 John 3:17-18)

_____

_____

_____

8) What are we to be diligent to preserve? *(Ephesians 4:3)*

_____

_____

_____

9) Why does Satan try to cause division? *(Luke 11:17)*

_____

_____

_____

- **Satan desires to divide and lay waste to God's Kingdom. One of his primary devices is to cause division by using people to tear down and devour one another through backbiting, thereby destroying the work of God.**

10) If we know that any brother has anything against us, what are we to do? *(Matthew 5:23-24)*

_____

_____

_____

11) What attitude should we have toward each other? *(Ephesians 4:32)*

_____

_____

_____

12) Is it God's will for us to walk alone in our service for Him? *(1 Corinthians 12:15-21)*

_____

_____

_____

13) Where has God placed each member? *(1 Corinthians 12:18)*

_____

_____

_____

THE IMPORTANCE OF BEING FITTED TOGETHER IN THE BODY OF CHRIST

Imagine a pair of eyes detached from the physical body. They are gruesome, and they serve no purpose when separated from the physical body. An eye connected

SESSION 12

100% of me belongs to Jesus, and He loves me. Song of Songs 7:10

to the body and in its proper place is a great asset because it gives sight to the whole body. The eye is also a beautiful thing to look at in the place where God has designed it to function. An eye apart from the body is dead and can do nothing. So it is in the body of Christ. A member of the body separate from the other members cannot function properly. It is dead, lifeless, and good for nothing. However, when that same member is attached to the rest of the body, it performs its proper function and blesses the entire body by being useful in the work of God.

14) How is the body joined and knit together? *(Ephesians 4:16)*

_____

_____

_____

15) As each joint is supplying that which it must give, what will happen? *(Ephesians 4:16)*

_____

_____

_____

16) What concept does this parable convey? *(Joel 2:7 – 11)*

_____

_____

_____

- **The Lord's army has unity, order, and discipline, which allows them to do great things for God.**

If this is the way unity is described for the church in infancy, consider how much more unity there should be in its maturity. Jesus is not coming for you individually. He is coming back for a glorious Church without spot or wrinkle – a church walking together in unity and love.

17) How is the manifold wisdom of God going to be revealed? (Ephesians 3:10)

---

18) To bear fruit, what must we do? (John 15:5)

NUGGETS

- Pray before you write out and share your story. Ask God for wisdom and the words to say.

- Write the way you speak.

- Be honest.

- Keep your story to about 1 ½ to three minutes so that it doesn't become a monologue that others want to be over.

- Practice your testimony out loud several times with your teacher until you feel comfortable sharing it.

HOMEWORK

Share the mission aloud with your partnering disciple, and then write it out using the space below. You will also rewrite the mission for homework in the back of the book.

ACTIVATION

Congratulations! You have spent the last 12 days learning about Jesus Christ, your Savior, His Kingdom, and what He expects from those who profess and follow Him.

Now it is time to get busy doing what He commanded--preach the Gospel, make disciples, baptize them, and teach them the ways of the Lord! This mission is the most exciting work you will ever do.

Review the names of the friends and family members listed in your Disciples Launchpad and decide with your teacher when you will go together to share the good news of Jesus Christ.

Your testimony is not the Gospel by itself. Remember to share the GOSPEL!

ANSWER KEY

1. We are one body with many members. (Romans 12: 4-5; 1 Corinthians 12:12-14)

2. We were baptized into one body. (1 Corinthians 12:13 – 14)

3. We are living stones and are being built up a spiritual house, a holy priesthood. (1 Peter 2:5, Ephesians 2:21 – 22)

4. Jesus said we should love one another as He has loved us. (John 13:34)

5. Jesus said all men would know we are His disciples if we have love for one another. (John 13:35)

6. Scripture says we should lay down our lives for our brothers. (1 John 3:16, John 15:13)

7. This love also expresses itself in commitment to each other in the following ways:

    a. Demonstrate loyalty and intense devotion to each other. (I Peter 4:8)

    b. Restrain from backbiting and devouring one another. (Galatians 5:15)

    c. Esteem your brother as better than yourself. (Philippians 2:3-4)

    d. Bear the burdens of the weak. Suffer with others. Rejoice when others are honored. (1 Corinthians 12:26, Romans 15:1)

    e. Love your enemies. (Matthew 5:44)

    f. Share your life with the brethren. (James 5:16, 1 Corinthians 12:25)

    g. Love in deed and help meet the needs of the brethren. (1 John 3:17-18)

8. We are to be diligent to preserve the unity of the Spirit in the bond of peace. (Ephesians 4:3)

9. Satan tries to cause division because he knows that a house divided against itself cannot stand, and a kingdom divided against itself is laid waste. (Luke 11:17)

10. We are to go and be reconciled to our brother. (Matthew 5:23 – 24)

11. We should be kind, tenderhearted, and forgiving to one another. (Ephesians 4:32)

12. No, it's not God's will for us to walk alone in our service for Him. (1 Corinthians 12:15 – 21)

13. God has placed each member in the body just as it pleases Him. (1 Corinthians 12:18)

14. The body is joined and knit together by what every joint supplies. (Ephesians 4:16)

15. The body will grow and build itself up in love. (Ephesians 4:16)

16. The Lord's army has unity, order, and discipline, which allows them to do great things for God. (Joel 2:7 – 11)

17. The manifold wisdom of God is to be revealed by the church. (Ephesians 3:10)

18. To bear fruit, we must abide in Jesus and relationship with His body. (John 15:5)

Additional Tools

100% of me belongs to Jesus, and He loves me. Song of Songs 7:10

The Gospel Message and the Mission

THE GOSPEL

"The Gospel is the good news that God became man in Jesus Christ; that He lived the life we should have lived and died the death we should have died because of our sin on the cross in our place. Three days later, He rose from the dead, just as He said, proving that He is the Son of God and offering the gift of the forgiveness of sins and eternal life (salvation) to all who, by faith, repent of their sins and receive Jesus Christ as both Lord and Savior."

THE MISSION

To become laid down lovers of God, servant lovers of all - one at a time, and make disciples who will do the same in every community, state, region, and nation.

Disciples Launchpad

Partnering Disciple Name: _____ Phone: _____

☐	Believed the Gospel of Jesus Christ	Date:_____
☐	Baptized in water	Date:_____
☐	Filled with the Holy Spirit	Date:_____
☐	Obtained a Bible and the Activated book	Date: _____
☐	Attended first church fellowship	Date:_____
☐	Activated book	Date (Start):_____ Date (End):_____
☐	Shared my testimony and the Gospel with my friends and family	Date:_____
☐	Assigned to a Piercing Sword Task Force	Date:_____
☐	Attended Get Connected meetting	Date:_____
☐	Starting praying for my VIP list	Date:_____

ADDITIONAL TOOLS

100% of me belongs to Jesus, and He loves me. Song of Songs 7:10

VIP Prayer List

Write out the names of 10 family members and friends who I am praying will be saved.

1. _____ Date:_____

2. _____ Date:_____

3. _____ Date:_____

4. _____ Date:_____

5. _____ Date:_____

6. _____ Date:_____

7. _____ Date:_____

8. _____ Date:_____

9. _____ Date:_____

10. _____ Date:_____

Bible Readings

Meditating on God's Word and obeying its teachings will bring success in life! God's word is reliable, without error, powerful, to the transforming of our hearts and mind. Below is a starter guide to begin getting into a habit of reading God's word daily. His word brings forth life! Get started reading His word.

☐ John	Date:_____
☐ Acts	Date:_____
☐ Galatians	Date:_____
☐ Ephesians	Date:_____
☐ Colossians	Date:_____
☐ 1 Peter	Date:_____
☐ 2 Peter	Date:_____
☐ 1 John	Date:_____
☐ 2 John	Date:_____
☐ 3 John	Date:_____
☐ *Proverbs	Date:_____
☐ **Psalms	Date:_____

* Proverbs: Read one chapter a day, correlating to the date. (ie. 3rd day of the month, read Proverbs 3)
** Psalms: Read the chapter correlated to the date, then add 30 to the chapter until you come to end. (i.e. 3rd day of the month, read Psalms 3, 33, 63, 93, 123)

My Testimony

Homework

100% of me belongs to Jesus, and He loves me. Song of Songs 7:10

HOMEWORK LESSON 1: THE ATONEMENT: GOD'S PROVISION FOR MAN'S SIN

1) What did Adam and Eve choose to do? *(Genesis 3:3-6)*

_____

_____

2) What was the temptation that drew them into sin? *(Genesis 3:5)*

_____

_____

3) Adam and Eve's sin was based on what three things? *(Genesis 3:6, I John 2:16)*

_____

_____

4) What was God doing in the garden, and what was the desire of His heart? *(Genesis 3:8-9*

_____

_____

5) What does the scripture teach about the spiritual condition of a man who willfully sins against God? *(Romans 3:10-19, 23)*

_____

_____

6) If all have sinned willfully and are *not* seeking God, then how can men come to God? *(Isaiah 19:20, John 6:44)*

_____

_____

7) Under the old covenant, how was man cleansed from sin and brought into a right relationship with God? *(Leviticus 16:14 - 15; 17:11)*

_____

_____

8) What did Jesus come to earth to do? *(Matthew 1:21, I John 3:5)*

_____

_____

9) What did John say when he saw Jesus coming toward him? *(John 1:29)*

_____

_____

10) What did Jesus do for us on the cross? *(I Peter 2:24, Galatians 3:13, Romans 6:6-7)*

_____

_____

11) What is the new covenant Jesus established and made available through His blood?

_____

_____

12) How can we become partakers of this new covenant? *(Acts 3:19, Romans 10:9-10)*

_____

_____

13) Why else did Jesus come to earth? *(John 3:16-17)*

_____

_____

14) Who is under God's judgment? *(John 3:18)*

_____

_____

15) What is God's desire toward us? *(2 Peter 3:9)*

_____

_____

100% of me belongs to Jesus, and He loves me. Song of Songs 7:10

HOMEWORK LESSON 2: WHO IS JESUS?

1) What was in the beginning, and who was it? *(John 1:1)*

_____

_____

2) Who became flesh and dwelt among us? *(John 1:14)*

_____

_____

3) Who was manifested in the flesh? *(1 Timothy 3:16)*

_____

_____

4) What were some of the things that people said about Jesus? *(John 7:40-41)*

_____

_____

5) What did Jesus say people search for in the scriptures? *(John 5:39)*

_____

_____

6) Jesus said the scriptures testify of whom? *(John 5:39)*

_____

_____

7) Why must a person come to Jesus? *(John 5:40)*

_____

_____

8) What problem did Peter have? *(Matthew 16:23)*

_____

_____

9) What did Jesus say had to be done before taking up your cross? *(Matthew 16:24)*

_____

_____

10) What does a person become after they sincerely deny themselves and take up their cross? *(Mark 8:34)*

_____

_____

11) What must you do if you want to save your life? *(Mark 8:35)*

_____

_____

12) How often should a person take up his cross? *(Luke 9:23)*

_____

_____

13) How often will you have to deny yourself if you are going to take up your cross daily? *(Luke 9:23)*

_____

_____

14) What did the rich young ruler think about Jesus? *(Mark 10:17)*

_____

_____

15) Did the rich young ruler live a good, moral life? How did Jesus feel about him *(Mark 10:19-21)?*

_____

_____

16) What did Jesus require of this young man in terms of self-denial before him taking up his cross and following Jesus? *(Mark 10:21)*

_____

_____

17) How did the rich young ruler respond? *(Mark 10:22)*

_____

_____

18) How did Jesus respond? *(Mark 10:23)*

_____

_____

MY LIFE BEFORE CHRIST

19) What about my life before Christ will relate most to the non-Christians with whom I am sharing?

- What sorts of sins did I struggle with?

_____

_____

- What did I think of Christianity?

_____

_____

- Was I raised in church?

_____

_____

- What life path was I on? Was it triumphant or tragic?

_____

_____

- What other appropriate information can I share that will accurately depict what my life was life before Christ?

_____

_____

20) What did my life revolve around, and name three things that were most important to me?

_____

_____

21) Where did I get my security, identity, or happiness?

_____

_____

22) In what ways do I see those things differently? How were they going to let me down?

_____

_____

HOMEWORK LESSON 3: THE LORDSHIP OF JESUS

1) According to Jesus, who are we to fear and why? *(Luke 12:5, Matthew 10:28)*

_____

_____

2) What judgment seat must we all appear before? *(2 Corinthians 5:10)*

_____

_____

3) What explanation does the scripture provide for persuading others to serve Jesus. *(2 Corinthians 5:11)*

_____

_____

4) In preaching the Gospel, what did Peter say about Jesus? *(Acts 2:36)*

_____

_____

5) When they heard this preaching, what happened and what was their response? *(Acts 2:37)*

_____

_____

6) What was Peter's response to the question asked? *(Acts 2:38)*

_____

_____

7) What are the rewards promised to those who have forsaken all to follow Christ? *(Matthew 19:27-29, Mark 10:28-30)*

_____

_____

8) Jesus gave the right to become _____ to those who _____ *(John 1:12)*

HOMEWORK

100% of me belongs to Jesus, and He loves me. Song of Songs 7:10

9) If we open our hearts to receive Jesus, what promise has He given us? *(Revelation 3:20)*

_____

_____

10) Unless one is born of _____ and the _____, he cannot enter the Kingdom of God. *(John 3:3-7)*

11) When we receive Jesus, what gift does God give? *(1 John 5:11; Romans 6:23)*

_____

_____

12) How does the Word of God define repentance *(Psalm 32:5; Proverbs. 28:13, Ezekiel 18:21-23,27-28)*?

_____

_____

13) If we confess our sins, what will God do? *(I John 1:9)*

_____

_____

14) If we are willing and obedient, what else will the Lord do? *(Isaiah 1:18-19)*

_____

_____

15) To live, what must the wicked man do? *(Ezekiel 33:15)*

_____

_____

16) What are the conditions set so God can dwell in us and walk among us? *(2 Corinthians 6:14-18)*

_____

_____

17) What did God require of the Israelites when they entered a land to possess it? *(Deuteronomy 7:1-3)*

_____

_____

18) Why did God require this? *(Deuteronomy 7:4,6; Deuteronomy 8:1)*

_____

_____

19) What happened to the son's life after he received his inheritance and left his father's house? *(Luke 15:11-16)*

_____

_____

20) What did the lost son decide to do when he realized his condition? *(Luke 15:17-19)*

_____

_____

21) When the son returned home, what did his father do? *(Luke 15:20)*

_____

_____

22) What happened after the son confessed his sin? *(Luke 15:22-24)*

_____

_____

23) When Jesus told Zacchaeus He would stay at his house, what was Zaccheus' response that showed his repentant heart? *(Luke 19: 1-8)*

_____

_____

24) What did Jesus say to Zaccheus? *(Luke 19:9-10)*

_____

_____

PERSONAL EXPERIENCE – HOW I CAME TO CHRIST

Question/Answer

1. When was the first time I heard the Gospel, and what was my initial reaction?

_____

_____

2. What did I realize when I heard it?

_____

_____

3. Why did I decide to give myself to Christ and give Him complete control of my life?

_____

_____

HOMEWORK LESSON 4: BECOMING A DISCIPLE

1) What two things did Jesus say His disciples would do? *(John 14:12)*

_____

_____

2) What is one of the ways disciples glorify the Father? *(John 15:8)*

_____

_____

3) As a disciple matures, who does he become more like? *(Luke 6:40)*

_____

_____

4) Who is the head of the church? *(Colossians 1:18, Ephesians 1:22)*

_____

_____

5) When a person becomes a disciple, who do they follow? *(1 Thessalonians 1:6)*

_____

_____

6) As followers of Christ, are you able to influence those who believe? *(1 Thessalonians 1:7)*

_____

_____

7) Who did Paul tell the disciples to follow, and under what conditions were they to do it? *(1 Corinthians 11:1)*

_____

_____

8) What was Paul's expectation of the disciples in Corinth? *(2 Corinthians 2:9)*

_____

_____

9) If someone loves Jesus, will they keep His commands and words? *(John 14:21, 23)*

_____

_____

HOMEWORK

100% of me belongs to Jesus, and He loves me. Song of Songs 7:10

10) How do you know if someone does not love Jesus? *(John 14:24)*

_____

_____

11) What requirement does Jesus make of friends? *(John 15:14)*

_____

_____

12) How is kingdom authority established? *(Luke 22:26-27, Matthew 20:26)*

_____

_____

13) Who is worthy of double honor? *(1 Timothy 5:17)*

_____

_____

14) What did the scribes say about Jesus, and what was His response? *(Mark 3:22, 28-30)*

_____

_____

15) What are believers instructed to do in this passage, and why? *(Hebrews 13:7, 17)*

_____

_____

16) What is better than sacrifice? *(1 Samuel 15:22)*

_____

_____

17) Whose authority did Jesus honor by answering the High Priest? *(Matthew 26:62-63)*

_____

_____

18) If a man wants you to do something contrary to God and His word, what should you do? *(Acts 5:29)*

_____

_____

HOMEWORK LESSON 5: GOD'S GOVERNMENT AND ORDER FOR THE CHURCH

1) What types of officials are set in the body of Christ to watch over and instruct the saints? And what are their responsibilities? *(Ephesians 4:11-12)*

_____

_____

2) How long will the ministry of the elders be in operation in the church? What will happen because of these ministries? *(Ephesians 4:13-15)*

_____

_____

3) What office of oversight has God appointed for the local church *(Acts 14:23)*

_____

_____

4) What are the responsibilities of the Elders? *(Acts 20:28, Hebrews 13:17)*

_____

_____

5) As a watchman of the flock of God, what specifically are the elders to do? *(Ezekl 33:2-7)*

_____

_____

6) If the watchman fails to warn the people, whose fault is it, and who is held accountable? *(Ezekiel 33:5-7)*

_____

_____

7) If the people under his oversight refused to take warning from their elders, who is responsible? *(Ezekiel 33:2-4)*

_____

_____

8) What are members of the body urged to do? *(Hebrews 13:17, I Peter 5:5)*

_____

_____

9) What should our attitude be toward those who are teaching us and leading us in the ways of God? *(Hebrews 13:7)*

_____

_____

10) What did the shepherd do when he realized one of his sheep had strayed away? *(Matthew 18:12)*

_____

_____

11) With whom are believers not to associate? *(I Corinthians 5:9–11)*

_____

_____

12) What did Paul say would happen if sin and evil behavior remains in the church? *(I Corinthians 5:1–6)*

_____

_____

13) Who are we to judge, and who does God judge? *(I Corinthians 5:12-13)*

_____

_____

14) What should you do if you know a member of the church is caught in unrepentant sin? *(Matthew 18:15 – 17)*

_____

_____

15) What are we to do with those "brothers/sisters" who refused to repent of their wickedness? *(I Corinthians 5:13)*

_____

_____

16) If a brother or sister is caught in sin and desires to be restored, how should they be treated? *(Galatians 6:1)*

_____

_____

17) What does Jesus say about removing those who will not repent, even if they are important members of the body? *(Matthew 5:29 – 30)*

_____

_____

18) What are the disciples urged to do? *(I Corinthians 5: 6-8)*

_____

_____

19) What happened to the Israelites who went up against Ai? *(Joshua 7:4-5)*

_____

_____

20) What reason did God give Joshua for this defeat? *(Joshua 7:11-12)*

_____

_____

21) What condition did God set before Israel for continuing to be with them? *(Josh 7:12-15)*

_____

_____

22) Why does God discipline us? *(Hebrews 12:5-10)*

_____

_____

23) What feeling do we have when we are disciplined, and what does discipline yield? *(Hebrews 12:11)*

_____

_____

100% of me belongs to Jesus, and He loves me. Song of Songs 7:10

MY LIFE AFTER COMING TO CHRIST

1. How is my life different now? List specific changes in your character, attitude, and perspective on life.

   _____

   _____

2. What motivates me now? What do I live for?

   _____

   _____

3. How does knowing Christ help me deal with challenges?

   _____

   _____

   _____

HOMEWORK LESSON 6: BAPTISM IN WATER

1) What was the circumcision a sign of under the old covenant? *(Genesis 17: 10 – 19)*

_____

_____

2) What is the circumcision of Christ? *(Colossians 2:11-12)*

_____

_____

3) How did Moses describe this true circumcision? *(Deuteronomy 30:6)*

_____

_____

4) How did Peter respond to the question asked after his sermon? *(Acts 2:38)*

_____

_____

5) What instructions did Jesus Christ leave for His Church? *(Matthew 28:19-20)*

_____

_____

6) What does Paul say about Israel's experience at the Red Sea? *(1 Corinthians 10:1-2)*

_____

_____

7) Why did Jesus partake of our flesh, blood, and death? *(Hebrews 2:14-15)*

_____

_____

8) How did the people respond when they received the Word of God? *(Acts 2:41)*

_____

_____

9) What did the people of Samaria do after they believed Philip's teaching? *(Acts 8:12)*

_____

_____

HOMEWORK

100% of me belongs to Jesus, and He loves me. Song of Songs 7:10

10) What did the Ethiopian eunuch desire after he heard the message about the Messiah? *(Acts 8:35-36)*

_____

_____

11) How was the eunuch baptized? *(Acts 8:38-39)*

_____

_____

12) What happened to the Philippian jailer and his family after believing Paul's message? *(Acts 16:29 – 33)*

_____

_____

13) How soon were the Philippian jailer and his family baptized? *(Acts 16:29 – 33)*

_____

_____

14) Through baptism, what two experiences do believers share with Christ? *(Romans 6:4)*

_____

_____

15) Since we are united with Him in the likeness of his death, what shall we also be? *(Romans 6:5)*

_____

_____

16) Many believers have gone through the motions of baptism yet have not experienced a genuine New Testament baptism. What have they experienced? *(Acts 19:3-4)*

_____

_____

HOMEWORK LESSON 7: BAPTISM IN THE HOLY SPIRIT

1) What did Jesus tell His disciples to do before they went out into the world to preach repentance? *(Luke 24:47 – 49)*

_____

_____

2) What was the "Promise of the Father" the disciples were to receive? *(Acts 1:4-5)*

_____

_____

3) What did Jesus say would happen when the Holy Spirit came upon them? *(Acts 1:8)*

_____

_____

4) Besides the 11 apostles, who else was waiting to receive the Holy Spirit's promise, and how many were present? *(Acts 1:13 – 15)*

_____

_____

5) What happened when the Holy Spirit was given? *(Acts 2: 1-4)*

_____

_____

_____

6) What did the tongues of fire represent? *(Matthew 3:11)*

_____

_____

7) Who was present in Jerusalem during the feast of Pentecost? *(Acts 2:5- 6)*

_____

_____

8) What did Peter explain to them? *(Acts 2:14 – 21)*

_____

_____

9) What instruction did Peter give to the people who were under conviction following his message at Pentecost? *(Acts 2:37 – 38)*

_____

_____

10) What did Jesus say about the Holy Spirit? *(John 14:16-17)*

_____

_____

11) What are two names given for the Holy Spirit? *(John 14:16-17)*

_____

_____

12) What other things did Jesus tell the disciples that the Holy Spirit would do for them? *(John 14:26, 15:26, 16:13)*

_____

_____

13) What did Paul say about the Gospel that he preached? *(I Corinthians 2:4)*

_____

_____

14) Where did Paul say the faith of men should rest? *(I Corinthians 2:5)*

_____

_____

15) How did Paul say that we might know the things God has given us? *(I Corinthians 2:9-12)*

_____

_____

16) What did Jesus say the Spirit would do for us when we are delivered up before the governors, kings, and those in authority? *(Matthew 10:18-20)*

_____

_____

17) What are we encouraged to do when we are delivered up for the defense of the Gospel? *(Matthew 10:19)*

_____

_____

18) How did Jesus fulfill his ministry? *(Acts 10:38)*

_____

_____

19) Describe the refining and purifying work that the Holy Spirit does. *(Malachi 3:1 – 3)*

_____

_____

20) What does Paul say the Spirit of the Lord has come to do? *(II Corinthians 3:18)*

_____

_____

21) How did the believers in Samaria receive the Holy Spirit? *(Acts 8:17)*

_____

_____

22) How did the believers in Ephesus receive the Holy Spirit, and what happened when the Holy Spirit came upon them? *(Acts 19:6)*

_____

_____

23) How did the Gentiles receive the Holy Spirit? *(Acts 10:44-46)*

_____

_____

24) How did those present know the Gentiles had received the Holy Spirit? *(Acts 10:45-46)*

_____

_____

HOMEWORK

100% of me belongs to Jesus, and He loves me. Song of Songs 7:10

25) What does the prophet Ezekiel say about the Holy Spirit when he is prophesying about the new covenant? *(Ezekiel 36:26 – 27)*

_____

_____

26) To whom is the promised gift of the Holy Spirit made available? *(Acts 2:39)*

_____

_____

27) To whom will the Father give the Holy Spirit? *(Luke 11:13)*

_____

_____

HOMEWORK LESSON 8: THE MISSION AND THE CHURCH

1) According to Jesus, what is the first and greatest commandment? *(Matthew 22:36-38)*

_____

_____

2) According to Jesus, what is the second greatest commandment? *(Matthew 22:39)*

_____

_____

3) How much of the law and the prophets would a person fulfill if they do these two things? *(Matthew 22:40)*

_____

_____

4) In the parable of the good Samaritan, what did the lawyer ask Jesus? *(Luke 10:25)*

_____

_____

5) What was Jesus' response to the lawyer when he answered with the first and second commandments? *(Luke 10:26-28)*

_____

_____

6) What is the first instruction given in this scripture? *(Matthew 28:19-20)*

_____

_____

7) What instructions did Jesus Christ leave for His Church? *(Matthew 28:19-20)*

_____

_____

8) Where did Jesus direct us to go, and what did He direct us to do? *(Mark 16:15)*

_____

_____

9) According to Jesus, who will be saved? *(Mark 16:16)*

_____

_____

10) After the disciples received the Holy Spirit, where did Jesus say they would first be witnesses of Him? *(Acts 1:8)*

_____

_____

11) What does Jerusalem represent? *(Acts 1:8)*

_____

_____

12) Who is the founder and builder of the Church? *(Matthew 16:18)*

_____

_____

13) Is Jesus Christ also the head of the church? *(Colossians 1:18)*

_____

_____

14) Who is the body of Christ? *(Colossians 1:24)*

_____

_____

15) What makes up the body of Christ? *(Romans 12:4-5; 1 Corinthians 12:12-14)*

_____

_____

16) What are we, and what are we being made into? *(1 Peter 2:5)*

_____

_____

17) How is the church described in this scripture? *(1 Peter 2:9-10)*

_____

_____

HOMEWORK LESSON 9: FINANCIAL PRINCIPLES

1) Who gives us the ability to produce wealth? *(Deuteronomy 8:18)*

_____

_____

2) What was promised to Israel if they obeyed God's commands? *(Deuteronomy 30:8-9)*

_____

_____

3) What happens when we give? *(Luke 6:38)*

_____

_____

4) How does the law of sowing and reaping apply to money? *(2 Corinthians 9:6)*

_____

_____

5) What is God able to do for the cheerful giver? *(2 Corinthians 9:7-8)*

_____

_____

6) Why does God provide riches for His people? *(2 Corinthians 9:11)*

_____

_____

7) What did Abraham do in response to the blessing of God? *(Genesis 14:18-20)*

_____

_____

8) If you belong to Christ, how are you related to Abraham, and what will you do?
   (Galatians 3:29, John 8:39)

_____

_____

9) What part should we give to God? *(Proverbs 3:9)*

_____

_____

10) How is the tithe described? How much of the increase goes to God? *(Leviticus 27:30-32)*

_____

_____

11) Should the tithe be an afterthought or forethought, and what will happen if you give the first part to God? *(Proverbs 3:9-10)*

_____

_____

12) According to Jesus' parable of the sower, what can choke out God's Word and cause it to be unfruitful? *(Mark 4:18 – 19)*

_____

_____

13) What are some of the worries of life that choke out God's Word? *(Matthew 6:25, 28, 31, 34)*

_____

_____

14) What should we guard ourselves against? *(Luke 12:15)*

_____

_____

15) For the love of _____ is a root of all kinds of evil. *(1 Timothy 6:10)*

16) It is impossible to serve both God and _____. *(Luke 16:13)*

17) Jesus never made such a statement about anything else. Why not?

_____

_____

18) What can happen to those who are eager for money and want to get rich? *(1 Timothy 6:9– 10)*

_____

_____

19) What can deliver us from death: righteousness or money? *(Proverbs 11:4)*

_____

_____

20) What happens to the one who trusts in money? *(Proverbs 11:28)*

_____

_____

21) What is the point of the parable of the rich fool? *(Luke 12:16 – 21)*

_____

_____

22) Where is your heart? *(Matthew 6:19-21)*

_____

_____

23) According to Jesus, who gave the most and why? *(Luke 21:1- 4)*

_____

_____

24) How much did the Macedonians give? *(2 Corinthians 8: 3)*

_____

_____

25) Did Paul have to pressure the Macedonian believers to give? *(2 Corinthians 8:4)*

_____

_____

26) What kind of giver are you?

_____

_____

27) Are you a faithful and grateful person who tithes?

_____

_____

HOMEWORK

100% of me belongs to Jesus, and He loves me. Song of Songs 7:10

28) Are you a person who gives with the right heart?

_____

_____

29) What changes must you make immediately?

_____

_____

THE MISSION

To become _____ _____ _____ of God, _____ lovers of all _____ _____ _____ _____, and _____ _____ who will do the _____ in every _____, _____, region and _____

HOMEWORKLESSON 10: THE LIFESTYLE OF A DISCIPLE OF JESUS CHRIST, PART 1

1) What is the nature of sin? (v. 13)

_____

_____

2) What will sin do to the person through its deceitfulness? (v. 13)

_____

_____

3) Is it possible for a believer to depart from the living God? (v. 12)

_____

_____

4) Why must a person guard themselves against this deception? (v. 12)

_____

_____

5) What causes the brethren to depart from the living God? (v. 12)

_____

_____

6) Who is responsible for keeping us away from being deceived and becoming hard-hearted? (v. 12)

_____

_____

7) Without the brethren, can one avoid the deception of sin?

_____

_____

8) What happens when we search for God? *(Jeremiah 29:13)*

_____

_____

9) What happens if we forsake Him? *(1 Chronicles 28:9)*

_____

_____

10) What happens when our mind is not on things above but on the places which we came from and worldly experiences we have had? *(Hebrews 11:13-16)*

_____

_____

11) Brethren, I do not count myself to have apprehended; but one thing I do, _____ those things which are _____ and _____ to those things which are _____, I _____ the _____ for the _____ of the upward call of God in Christ Jesus. *(Philippians 3:13-14)*

12) Does a good soldier, engaged in warfare, entangle himself in the affairs of life? *(2 Timothy 2:4)*

_____

_____

13) Why doesn't a good soldier engage himself in the affairs of life? *(2 Timothy 2:4)*

_____

_____

14) What should our attitude be towards the affiliations and sufferings we experience in life? *(2 Corinthians 4:17; Romans 8:18)*

_____

_____

15) What did Jesus say His disciples would do? *(Matthew 9:15)*

_____

_____

16) While Jesus was walking with His disciples, why didn't they fast? *(Mark 2:20)*

_____

_____

17) According to Jesus, what would lead His disciples to fast? *(Luke 5:35)*

_____

_____

18) Along with their faith, what else did Jesus say was needed for the young boy to be free? *(Matthew 17:20-21)*

_____

_____

HOMEWORK

100% of me belongs to Jesus, and He loves me. Song of Songs 7:10

HOMEWORK LESSON 11: THE LIFESTYLE OF A DISCIPLE OF JESUS CHRIST, PART 2

1) What does the Bible say about swearing falsely (vows) and oaths? *(Matthew 5:33 – 36)*

_____

_____

2) How are we to respond to certain questions, and why? *(Matthew 5:37)*

_____

_____

3) For out of the abundance of the heart _____. *(Matthew 12:34-35)*

4) What will happen to us for speaking idle words? *(Matthew 12:36)*

_____

_____

5) How shall we be justified, and how shall we be condemned? *(Matthew 12:37)*

_____

_____

6) A _____ answer turns away wrath, but a _____ word stirs up anger. *(Proverbs 15:1)*

7) The words of a man's mouth are _____ waters; the wellspring of _____ is a _____. *(Proverbs 18:4)*

8) When we are persecuted for the sake of Christ and His Kingdom, how should we respond? *(Matthew 5:10 – 12)*

_____

_____

9) Read Matthew 5:22 and see what Jesus says about murder in the heart. "But I say to you that whoever is _____ with his _____ shall be in danger of the _____. And whoever says to his brother, _____ shall be in danger of the _____. But whoever says, _____ shall be in danger of _____".

10) What should your attitude be toward one who mistreats or slaps you? *(Matthew 5:39)*

_____

_____

11) While some have said it is okay to hate your enemies, what does Jesus say? *(Matthew 5:43-47)*

_____

_____

12) How does God demonstrate this type of love? *(Matthew 5:45)*

_____

_____

13) If you love only those who love you, is that any credit to you? *(Luke 6:32 – 33)*

_____

_____

14) _____, and you shall not be judged. Condemn not, and you shall _____. Forgive, and you _____. *(Luke 6:37)*

15) Amid persecution, how did Jesus respond? *(1 Peter 2:23)*

_____

_____

16) How often are you to forgive others? *(Matthew 18:21 – 22)*

_____

_____

17) If you present your offering to God and remember your brother has something against you, what are you to do? *(Matthew 5:23 – 24)*

_____

_____

18) If you do not forgive others, what attitude does the Father take toward you? *(Matthew 6:14 – 15)*

_____

_____

100% of me belongs to Jesus, and He loves me. Song of Songs 7:10

19) How are you to treat others? *(Matthew 7:12; Luke 6:31)*

_____

_____

20) What does Jesus teach us about humility? *(Luke 18:10 – 14)*

_____

_____

21) When _____ comes, then comes shame; But with the _____ is wisdom.
    (Proverbs 11:2)

22) Likewise you younger people, _____ yourselves to your elders. Yes, all of you
    be submissive to one another, and be clothed with _____, for "God _____
    the proud, But gives _____ to the humble." *(1 Peter 5:5)*

23) If you desire to be great and first in the Kingdom, what posture should you take
    before others? *(Matthew 20:26 – 28)*

_____

_____

24) What is the greatest sign of love? *(John 15:13)*

_____

_____

25) What should be your attitude toward giving to others? *(Luke 6:29 – 30, 34 – 35)*

_____

_____

26) What did Jesus say for us to do if we love him? *(John 21:15 – 17)*

_____

_____

27) How are we expected to show love to the brethren in need? *(Matthew 25:35 – 40)*

_____

_____

28) How are we expected to love one another? *(1 John 3:16 – 18)*

_____

_____

29) What did Jesus say about faithfulness? *(Luke 16:10)*

_____

_____

30) What did Jesus say about the unjust? *(Luke 16:10)*

_____

_____

31) Who did Apostle Paul say to commit the work? *(2 Timothy 2:2)*

_____

_____

100% of me belongs to Jesus, and He loves me. Song of Songs 7:10

HOMEWORK LESSON 12: COMMITMENT TO THE BODY OF CHRIST

1) What makes up the body of Christ? *(Romans 12: 4-5; 1 Corinthians 12:12-14)*

_____

_____

2) As children of God, what were we baptized into? *(1 Corinthians 12:13-14)*

_____

_____

3) What are we, and what are we corporately being built into? *(1 Peter 2:5, Ephesians 2:21-22)*

_____

_____

4) How did Jesus say we are to love one another? *(John 13:34)*

_____

_____

5) By what sign did Jesus say all men would know we are His disciples? *(John 13:35)*

_____

_____

6) In defining that love, what do the scriptures say? *(1 John 3:16, John 15:13)*

_____

_____

7) This love also expresses itself in commitment to each other in the following ways:

    a. (1 Peter 4:8)

_____

_____

    b. (Galatians 5:15)

_____

_____

c. (Philippians 2:3-4)

_____

_____

d. (1 Corinthians 12:26, Romans 15:1)

_____

_____

e. (Matthew 5:44)

_____

_____

f. (James 5:16, 1 Corinthians 12:25)

_____

_____

g. (1 John 3:17-18)

_____

_____

8) What are we to be diligent to preserve? *(Ephesians 4:3)*

_____

_____

9) Why does Satan try to cause division? *(Luke 11:17)*

_____

_____

10) If we know that any brother has anything against us, what are we to do? *(Matthew 5:23-24)*

_____

_____

11) What attitude should we have toward each other? *(Ephesians 4:32)*

_____

_____

12) Is it God's will for us to walk alone in our service for Him? *(1 Corinthians 12:15-21)*

_____

_____

13) Where has God placed each member? *(1 Corinthians 12:18)*

_____

_____

14) How is the body joined and knit together? *(Ephesians 4:16)*

_____

_____

15) As each joint is supplying that which it must give, what will happen? *(Ephesians 4:16)*

_____

_____

16) What concept does this parable convey? *(Joel 2:7 – 11)*

_____

_____

17) How is the manifold wisdom of God going to be revealed? *(Ephesians 3:10)*

_____

_____

18) To bear fruit, what must we do? *(John 15:5)*

_____

_____

Disciples Launchpad

Partnering Disciple Name: _____ Phone: _____

☐	Believed the Gospel of Jesus Christ	Date:_____
☐	Baptized in water	Date:_____
☐	Filled with the Holy Spirit	Date:_____
☐	Obtained a Bible and the Activated book	Date: _____
☐	Attended first church fellowship	Date:_____
☐	Activated book	Date (Start):_____ Date (End):_____
☐	Shared my testimony and the Gospel with my friends and family	Date:_____
☐	Assigned to a Piercing Sword Task Force	Date:_____
☐	Attended Get Connected meetting	Date:_____
☐	Starting praying for my VIP list	Date:_____

Made in the USA
Las Vegas, NV
04 January 2024

83834301R00096